CHEMISTRY FOR BIOLOGISTS

Chemistry
for Biologists

J. G. Stamper
M.A., D.Phil. (Oxon)
Lecturer in Chemistry, University of Sussex

M. A. Stamper
B.Sc., Dip.Ed.
Tutor in Biology, Wolsey Hall, Oxford

London · George Allen & Unwin Ltd
Ruskin House   Museum Street

First published in 1971

© George Allen & Unwin Ltd, 1971

ISBN 0 04 540006 7

Set in cold type by E.W.C. Wilkins & Associates Ltd
and printed in Great Britain by Alden & Mowbray Ltd
at the Alden Press, Oxford

Introduction

Modern biology is becoming ever more biochemical. Nowhere is this more apparent than in the syllabuses for the various 'O' and 'A' level examinations. A few years ago it was possible for someone to obtain 'O' and 'A' level passes and even a degree in biology without any knowledge of chemistry. This is no longer so, but because there are still many people with little or no chemical background studying biology for, in particular, 'A' level, we have written this book in the hope that it will be of use to them.

It is not a textbook of chemistry. The chemist or the biochemist will find many simplifications and lacunae. What we have tried to do is to present those ideas, concepts and facts of chemistry, elementary or advanced, that are immediately relevant to school biology, in a way that will be consistent and comprehensible even to the student who is unsure of the meaning of 'molecule'.

Many of the branches of chemistry that are of biological interest fall outside the subject as it is usually taught in schools. We therefore hope that some parts of this book, especially Chapter 5, may be of interest and help to students of biology who are also studying chemistry.

As an aid to understanding we have included a few problems in the text. Worked solutions for all of them are given on pp. 89–92 and their results are occasionally referred to at a later stage.

Ringmer 1970

M.A.S.
J.G.S.

Contents

CHAPTER 1

Atoms and Molecules

1. *Elements and compounds*

All matter is made up of *atoms* which are the smallest particles of
matter to have distinct chemical properties. Atoms themselves are made
up of other, simpler particles, as we shall see later in this chapter, but
for most chemical purposes atoms can be considered as the 'building
blocks' from which matter is constructed. If a substance is made up of
atoms of one kind only it is called an *element* so that there are as many
different elements as there are kinds of atom – in fact about 100.

In classical and medieval times matter was often thought to be made
up of four elements only (earth, air, fire and water). When the modern
concept of a large number of elements superseded this, about 200
years ago, an element was not defined in terms of atoms as we have
done, but as a simple substance which cannot be split up into any
simpler substances. This is not an easy criterion to apply since the
simplicity of a substance is not easily recognizable: chlorine, which is
now a familiar element, was thought for some time after its discovery
to contain the element oxygen. The two definitions are not really
contradictory, for any attempt to decompose an element into simpler
substances would require the break-up of the atoms themselves.

Although, in the last thirty years, the transformation of one kind of
atom into another has become an almost commonplace procedure, it
could not be carried out by the methods available to eighteenth- and
nineteenth-century chemists. From their point of view, then, the two
definitions of an element would be equivalent – and both have their
advantages. The definition in terms of atoms is ultimately more
satisfactory because, although it is further removed from experiment,
it takes account of the possibility of atoms' being transformed into
one another.

A few elements are familiar in everyday life. Air, for example, as we

1

shall see later, consists of a mixture mainly of the elements nitrogen and oxygen. Most metals are elements (e.g. iron, aluminium, copper) though the metals actually used commercially usually contain small amounts of other elements which make the metals harder or more resistant to corrosion.

If a substance contains atoms of more than one kind it may be a chemical compound or a mixture. In a *compound* the various elements are present in definite proportions and cannot be separated by simple physical means such as distillation or solution and filtration. In a *mixture*, on the other hand, the elements can be present in variable proportions, and a mixture can usually be separated by physical means into its component elements or compounds.

The majority of the substances familiar in everyday life are mixtures, though in many of them one particular compound is present in a much larger proportion than the others. Water is a compound of the elements hydrogen and oxygen; common salt (chemically called sodium chloride) is a compound of sodium and chlorine; chalk (the rock, not blackboard chalk) and limestone consist almost entirely of calcium carbonate, a compound of calcium, carbon and oxygen.

Almost all common biological materials, on the other hand, are complex mixtures. Before the chemistry of many compounds of biological importance can be studied, lengthy and tedious separations from the many other compounds present in a living tissue have to be carried out. The recent remarkable advances in biochemistry, as this branch of science is called, have, to a considerable extent, been due to the development of new and powerful techniques for separating the compounds in such mixtures.

2. *Molecules*

We must now consider the ways in which the atoms which make up elements, compounds and mixtures are arranged. In a great many cases small numbers of atoms are fastened together into aggregates called *molecules*. The atoms within a molecule are held together by rather strong forces called *chemical bonds*, or just *bonds*, while the molecules are held together by weaker forces of various kinds. (We shall say something about the description of the strengths of forces between atoms in the next chapter.) In a compound all the molecules present are of the same kind, which is why the various elements are present in definite proportions. A molecule of water, for example, contains two hydrogen atoms and one oxygen atom, as shown in Fig. 1.1a. A sample of water will consist of a very large number of identical water molecules

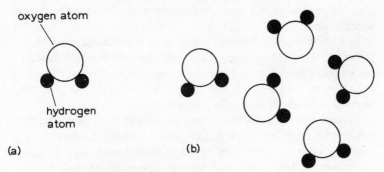

Fig. 1.1 Schematic diagrams of
(a) a single water molecule
(b) a sample of water containing a number of molecules (in fact 5). There are 5 oxygen atoms and 10 hydrogen atoms so that the ratio of hydrogen to oxygen is still 2:1.

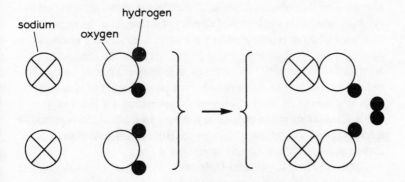

Fig. 1.2 Schematic diagram of the reaction between sodium and water to form sodium hydroxide and hydrogen.

and so there must be two hydrogen atoms for every oxygen atom present in the sample. Any sample of water, therefore, contains hydrogen and oxygen in the ratio 2:1 (as shown in Fig. 1.1b) if the amounts are measured by numbers of atoms. Different kinds of atoms have different weights, as we shall see shortly, so that if the ratio is measured by weight it is not 2:1 but is still constant (1:8 in fact). The chemical properties of a compound are the properties of the molecules which make it up.

In a mixture several kinds of molecule are present. They can be present in various proportions, and so the elements of which they are made up can also be present in various proportions. Further, the molecules are held together only by weak forces, so that only simple physical methods are needed to separate them.

In some free elements also, expecially gaseous ones, the atoms are combined into molecules. Hydrogen gas for example, consists of molecules each containing two hydrogen atoms joined together. In other cases, such as metals, each atom is surrounded by a number of other identical ones and is not especially associated with any of them so that the idea of a molecule of the element cannot be applied.

3. *Formulae and equations*

The way in which the molecule of a compound is made up of atoms is indicated by its *chemical formula*. The different atoms are denoted by symbols, which are single letters or pairs of letters, and the number of each kind of atom is indicated by a subscript number. The symbols for hydrogen and oxygen are H and O respectively and the chemical formula for water, with two atoms of hydrogen and one of oxygen in each molecule, is H_2O. The symbols for a large number of elements, including almost all those of biological importance, are listed in Table 1.1. Making use of that table it is easy to see that the formula for calcium carbonate, whose molecules contain one calcium atom, one carbon atom and three oxygen atoms, is $CaCO_3$.

Chemical formulae, besides their use as a shorthand notation for the composition of molecules, are also used in *chemical equations*. Perhaps the most important properties of any chemical element or compound are its *reactions,* that is to say the ways in which it may be transformed

TABLE 1.1

Some Chemical Elements, their Symbols and Atomic Weights

Element	Symbol	Atomic weight	Element	Symbol	Atomic weight
Aluminium	Al	27	Iron	Fe	55·8
Argon	A	39·9	Krypton	Kr	83·8
Arsenic	As	74·9	Lithium	Li	6·9
Beryllium	Be	9	Magnesium	Mg	24·3
Boron	B	10·8	Manganese	Mn	54·9
Bromine	Br	79·9	Neon	Ne	20·2
Calcium	Ca	40·1	Nickel	Ni	58·7
Carbon	C	12	Nitrogen	N	14
Chlorine	Cl	35·5	Oxygen	O	16
Chromium	Cr	52	Phosphorus	P	31
Cobalt	Co	58·9	Potassium	K	39·1
Copper	Cu	63·5	Scandium	Sc	45
Fluorine	F	19	Selenium	Se	79
Gallium	Ga	69·7	Silicon	Si	28·1
Germanium	Ge	72·6	Sodium	Na	23
Helium	He	4	Sulphur	S	32·1
Hydrogen	H	1	Zinc	Zn	65·4
Iodine	I	126·9			

into other chemical compounds. Reactions may be brought about in many ways, the commonest of which are heating and interaction with other compounds. Chemical equations are a shorthand way of representing these reactions. The formulae for elements or compounds which are undergoing the reaction are written on the left hand side of an 'equals' sign, and the formulae for the elements or compounds produced (the *products*) are written on the right. We can best illustrate this with an example.

The element sodium, which is a metal though not commonly to be met with as the free element, reacts very vigorously with water. Hydrogen gas bubbles off and the compound sodium hydroxide, whose molecules contain one atom each of sodium, oxygen and hydrogen, remains. This reaction can be represented by the equation

$$2Na \quad + \quad 2H_2O \quad = \quad 2NaOH \quad + \quad H_2$$

sodium   water   sodium   hydrogen
                             hydroxide

There are several points to be noticed in this equation. The names of the various substances involved here have been printed underneath to help you to follow the equation; they are not usually included in this way. Some of the formulae have numbers written in front of them. These imply that more than one molecule of a given kind takes part in the reaction. In this case, two sodium atoms react with two molecules of water to form two molecules of sodium hydroxide and one of hydrogen.

These numbers can be inferred from the fact that there must be the same number of atoms on each side of the equation — because in any chemical process atoms are never destroyed or transformed, but only rearranged into other compounds. The way in which this takes place for the reaction of sodium with water is shown in Fig. 1.2. The process of ensuring that there are equal numbers on each side is called *balancing* the equation and it is conventional to keep the number of molecules as small as possible, so that we write the equation as above rather than, for example, as

$$4Na + 4H_2O = 4NaOH + 2H_2$$

The balancing of an equation can be illustrated for the biologically important reaction of glucose with oxygen from which almost all living organisms derive the energy (see Chapter 2) which they need. The formula for glucose is $C_6H_{12}O_6$ and for oxygen O_2; the products of their reaction are water and carbon dioxide (CO_2). The first attempt at writing down the equation might be

$$C_6H_{12}O_6 + O_2 = CO_2 + H_2O$$

which clearly does not balance. The easiest way to start balancing is to find an atom which appears in only one formula on each side and to adjust the equation so that equal numbers of this atom appear on each side. Carbon (C) is such an atom. There are six carbons on the left, so we shall need six on the right which we can get by putting a six in front of CO_2.

$$C_6H_{12}O_6 + O_2 = 6\,CO_2 + H_2O$$

Hydrogen (H) also appears in only one formula on each side, so we next adjust the equation to balance for hydrogen — twelve atoms on each side.

$$C_6H_{12}O_6 + O_2 = 6\,CO_2 + 6\,H_2O$$

Finally there are eighteen oxygen atoms on the right (twelve in $6\,CO_2$ and six in $6\,H_2O$) and only eight on the left. We do not want to disturb the C and H which we have got right, so we complete the process by putting a six in front of O_2 since six of the eighteen are accounted for in $C_6H_{12}O_6$

$$C_6H_{12}O_6 + 6\,O_2 = 6\,CO_2 + 6\,H_2O$$

Problem 1.1.* Balance the equation below for the anaerobic degradation of glucose to ethanol (C_2H_6O) and carbon dioxide (also an important source of energy for some organisms).

$$C_2H_{12}O_6 = C_2H_6O + CO_2$$

Balancing an equation is not just an academic excercise; it enables us to deduce additional information from the equation — in the case of the reaction of glucose with oxygen we can see that each molecule of glucose will react with exactly six molecules of oxygen to form exactly six molecules of carbon dioxide and six molecules of water.

It is possible to go further than this, for the weights of all the atoms involved are known. Thus it is possible to calculate the weights of the various compounds that react. In fact we do not need the actual weights but only the relative weights of the different atoms — the so-called *atomic weights* which are listed in Table 1.1.

Hydrogen is the lightest atom and is given an atomic weight of 1. A carbon atom weighs 12 times as much as a hydrogen atom and so its atomic weight is 12. That of oxygen is 16. A molecule of glucose, therefore, weighs 160 times the weight of an atom of hydrogen. (Six carbon atoms weighing 12 times H — 72; six oxygen atoms weighing 16 times H — 96; twelve hydrogen atoms — 12; 72 + 96 + 12 = 160.) This is called the *molecular weight* of glucose. The molecular weight of

* Worked answer on p.89.

oxygen is 32, of carbon dioxide 44 and of water 18. Now we can take
the unit of weight to be whatever we like — the gramme (g) for instance.
If we do, the equation shows that 160 g of glucose react with
192 g (6 × 32 g) of oxygen to form 26 g (6 × 44 g) of oxygen and
108 g (6 × 18 g) of water. The molecular weight in grammes which we
have used here is of frequent occurrence and is called the *gramme
molecule*, or *mole*.

Problem 1.2.* Using atomic weights from Table 1.1, calculate the
weights of sodium and water needed to form 2 g of hydrogen,
according to the equation

$$2\,Na + 2\,H_2O = 2\,NaOH + H_2$$

4. *The structure of atoms*

We want now to consider in rather greater detail the way in which
atoms are linked together in molecules and to see why, for example,
the water molecule contains two atoms of hydrogen to each oxygen
rather than some other number. As a preliminary to this we must
consider the structure of atoms themselves.

All atoms are made up of two parts — a very small, heavy *nucleus*
carrying a positive electric charge, surrounded by a number of much
lighter *electrons* carrying negative charges. The electrons in all atoms
are indistinguishable, but the nucleus varies in both charge and weight
from one kind of atom to another. From a chemical point of view the
most important property of the nucleus is its electrical charge. This is
always equal to a whole number (called the *atomic number* and usually
represented by the letter Z) times the charge of the electron and
determines the chemical properties of the atom.

To be more accurate, it is, as we shall see, the number of electrons
in an atom which determines its chemical properties, but since atoms as
a whole are electrically neutral, the number of electrons is just equal
to the atomic number.

Atoms are, of course, extremely small and numerous. For example,
one gramme of iron contains about 120 000 000 000 000 000 000 000

* Worked answer on p.89.

atoms so that the weight of a single iron atom is
0·000 000 000 000 000 000 000 008 3 g. Of this weight only about 1/2 000
is made up of electrons. The size of an atom is a quantity which cannot
be defined very accurately, but the distance of closest approach of the
centres (i.e. the nuclei) of the atoms in a piece of iron is about
0·000 000 02 cm. The nucleus is very much smaller, though its size is
equally difficult to define. The diameter of an atom is about 10 000
times as great as the diameter of its nucleus.

We can see, therefore, that most of an atom is made up of space. In
this space the electrons move in a way which cannot be described
exactly except in mathematical terms. However, for many chemical
purposes it is sufficient to think of the electrons as being grouped in
shells of successively increasing size, not unlike the orbits of planets
around the sun.

These shells have the important property of only being able to
accomodate a limited number of electrons—the number increasing
with the size of the shell in a way which appears very irregular, but
which is well understood in terms of the details of electronic motion.
The shells are designated by letters, K being the smallest, and successively
larger ones being called L,M,N, etc. The K-shell can accomodate up to
two electrons, the L-shell eight, the M-shell eight, the N-shell eighteen,
and so on. If we know the atomic number of an atom, we can easily
work out the shell structure of its electrons. For example, the hydrogen
atom, which is the simplest of all, has an atomic number of one, so
contains only a single electron, which is in the K-shell. Oxygen, with an
atomic number of eight, has eight electrons, two of which are
accommodated in the K-shell which is then filled, while the other six
go into the L-shell. Table 1.2 lists the first thirty six elements in order
of atomic number and indicates their electronic structure.

The important feature of this shell structure from the chemical
point of view is that a completely filled shell (or '*closed*' *shell*) is a
particularly stable situation, and that atoms enter into combination
with each other in various ways in order to achieve such a situation.

5. *The periodic table*

The chemical properties of an element depend primarily on the number

TABLE 1.2

Element	Chemical symbol	Atomic number (Z)	Electronic structure			
			K-shell	L-shell	M-shell	N-shell
Hydrogen	H	1	1			
Helium	He	2	2			
Lithium	Li	3	2	1		
Beryllium	Be	4	2	2		
Boron	B	5	2	3		
Carbon*	C	6	2	4		
Nitrogen*	N	7	2	5		
Oxygen*	O	8	2	6		
Fluorine	F	9	2	7		
Neon	Ne	10	2	8		
Sodium*	Na	11	2	8	1	
Magnesium*	Mg	12	2	8	2	
Aluminium	Al	13	2	8	3	
Silicon*	Si	14	2	8	4	
Phosphorus*	P	15	2	8	5	
Sulphur*	S	16	2	8	6	
Chlorine*	Cl	17	2	8	7	
Argon	A	18	2	8	8	
Potassium*	K	19	2	8	8	1
Calcium*	Ca	20	2	8	8	2
Scandium	Sc	21	2	8	8	3
Titanium	Ti	22	2	8	8	4
Vanadium	V	23	2	8	8	5
Chromium	Cr	24	2	8	8	6
Manganese	Mn	25	2	8	8	7
Iron*	Fe	26	2	8	8	8
Cobalt	Co	27	2	8	8	9
Nickel	Ni	28	2	8	8	10
Copper*	Cu	29	2	8	8	11
Zinc*	Zn	30	2	8	8	12
Gallium	Ga	31	2	8	8	13
Germanium	Ge	32	2	8	8	14

Element	Chemical symbol	Atomic number (Z)	Electronic structure K-shell	L-shell	M-shell	N-shell
Arsenic	As	33	2	8	8	15
Selenium	Se	34	2	8	8	16
Bromine	Br	35	2	8	8	17
Krypton	Kr	36	2	8	8	18

of electrons in the outermost shell of the atom of that element, and especially on how close to the stable closed shell structure it is. The same kind of structure occurs with several different elements as sucessive shells are filled up, and we might expect that elements whose atoms have the same kind of structure, would also have closely similar chemical properties. This is indeed so — for example, the elements sodium and potassium both have one electron outside a closed shell and they are chemically very similar. These similarities are conveniently displayed in diagrammatic form by the *periodic table* (Fig. 1.3). In this table the elements are arranged in rows (called *periods*)

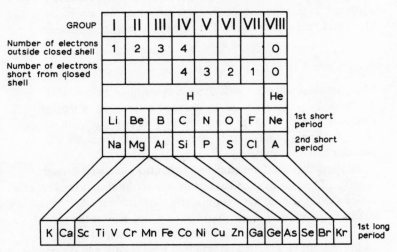

Fig. 1.3 The periodic table.

in order of atomic number i.e. of increasing number of electrons, a new row being started after each closed shell. In each column of the table (called a *group*) the atoms all have similar electronic structures, and consequently similar chemical properties. All the elements in Group I, for example, have atoms with one electron outside closed shells; all those in Group VI need two electrons to make up a closed shell. Hydrogen is not allotted to any group because its structure is unique, being simultaneously one electron short of a closed shell and having only one electron in its outer shell. Its chemistry is similarly unique.

As the L- and M-shells can both contain eight electrons, the first two periods (the *short* periods) of the table where the two shells are being filled up, each contain eight elements. The N-shell can contain eighteen electrons os that the next period of the table contains eighteen elements (the *long* period). The ones near the beginning of the period have only a small number of electrons outside closed shells and are therefore chemically similar to the elements near the beginnings of the short periods. Those near the end of the long period have structures close to a closed shell and so they are chemically similar to the elements near the ends of the short periods. The elements in the middle of the long period (scandium to zinc) have structures far removed from closed shells and so they are chemically quiet different from any of the elements in the short periods. They are called *transition* elements.

6. Ionic compounds

There are three ways in which an atom can achieve a closed shell structure: by losing electrons, by gaining electrons, or by sharing electrons. The first two are complementary since if one atom loses an electron, the electron is usually gained by another atom. We will consider these two first.

Suppose that a sodium atom and a chlorine atom were brought together. The sodium atom has one more electron than is needed for a closed shell structure, while the chlorine atom has one electron too few to form a closed shell. Each atom can therefore achieve the stability of a closed shell situation if one electron is transferred from the sodium to the chlorine (Fig. 1.4). This is indeed what occurs, and the process has an additional important result. The sodium atom, having lost an electron, no longer has sufficient electrons to balance the positive

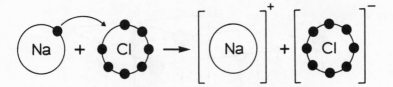

Fig. 1.4 Schematic diagram showing transfer of an
electron in the formation of sodium and choride ions.
Closed shells of electrons are omitted.

charge of the nucleus, so that the atom as a whole acquires a net
positive charge. The chlorine atom, on the other hand, now has one
negatively charged electron more than is needed to balance its nuclear
charge, so that the atom as a whole acquires a net negative charge.
Atoms with net charges of this kind are refered to as *ions*. An atom
with one or more electrons missing (net positive charge) is called a
positive ion or sometimes a *cation* and an atom with one or more excess
electrons (net negative charge) is called a *negative ion* or *anion*. Ions are
often denoted by the symbol of the element with the charge on the ion
written as a superscript. A sodium ion is thus represented by Na^+, for
example and a chlorine* ion by Cl^-.

An important result of these opposite charges is that the two ions
attract one another strongly, and it is this attraction which forms the
bond in sodium chloride. This sort of attraction is not specific, however.
One sodium ion can attract a number of chlorine ions if they are there
to be attracted, and equally one chlorine ion can attract a number of
sodium ions. In a crystal of sodium chloride they do just this, and the
crystal consists of an almost endless series of alternating sodium and
chlorine ions in three dimensions, each positive ion being surrounded by
six negatives ions and vice versa (Fig. 1.5).

In such a compound we cannot strictly speak of molecules of
sodium chloride, and the constancy of composition does not therefore
arise from the numbers of atoms in the molecule. Instead it is
guaranteed by the fact that the formation of each chloride ion requires
one electron, which is produced in the formation of one sodium ion,
so that the numbers of sodium and chlorine atoms or ions in the

* The Cl⁻ ion is usually called a chloride ion because compounds containing it are
called chlorides.

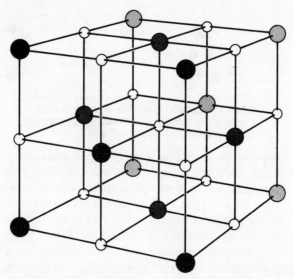

Fig. 1.5 Schematic diagram of a part of a sodium chloride
crystal. The ions have been represented by small symbols
for clarity. In fact they are large enough to touch each
other. Dark circles, Cl^-; open circles Na^+

crystal must be equal. The statement we made earlier that the sodium
chloride molecule contains an atom each of sodium and chlorine is thus
an over-simplification – though it is actually true at very high temperatures when sodium chloride is a gas.

There remains the problem of how to represent compounds like
sodium chloride in a chemical equation. Conventionally this is done by
writing the simplest formula which represents the composition of the
crystals – in this case NaCl. Such a formula is called the *empirical
formula* of the compound.

Ionic compounds of this kind always result when an element whose
atom contains few electrons (1, 2, sometimes 3) outside a closed shell,
forms a compound with an element with an almost closed shell
structure (1 or 2 electrons short of a closed shell); that is to say, when
an atom from the left hand side of the periodic table forms a compound
with one from the right hand side of the table. The numbers of atoms
of each element present in the compound are not always equal as they

are in the case of sodium chloride. If the number of electrons which one atom has to lose is different from the number the other has to gain, the atoms will combine in unequal numbers. For example, oxygen with six electrons in the L-shell needs two electrons to form a closed shell structure and the oxygen ion* is thus O^{2-}. If sodium combines with oxygen, therefore, two sodium atoms (each with one electron outside a closed shell) are needed to provide sufficient electrons for each oxygen atom, and the resulting compound, called sodium oxide, can be represented by the empirical formula Na_2O.

Problem 1.3. Using arguments like those of the last section, deduce the empirical formulae of calcium chloride and aluminium oxide.

7. Covalent compounds

As the number of electrons removed from or added to an atom increases, the process becomes increasingly difficult. Removing one electron from an atom leaves a positively charged ion which holds the remaining electrons more tightly; adding one electron to an atom forms a negatively charged ion which tends to repel additional electrons if they try to add on to it. There is, therefore, a limit to the number of electrons which can be completely transferred in this way and elements in the centre of the periodic table with atomic structures far removed from closed shells have to find some other way of forming compounds. They do it by sharing electrons.

The simplest possible case is that of the hydrogen molecule which, as we saw earlier, contains two hydrogen atoms. Each atom has one electron, so that both can achieve the stable closed shell (which contains only two electrons in the case of the K-shell) by sharing the two electrons between them, as shown in Fig. 1.6. This kind of behaviour is very common, especially in the chemistry of compounds of biological importance, and is called *covalent bonding* — the atoms being joined by a *covalent bond*.

We want now to consider a rather more complicated case of covalent bonding — that between carbon and hydrogen. Carbon and hydrogen form a number of compounds of which the simplest, methane, contains

---

* The O^{2-} ion is usually called the oxide ion since compounds containing it are called oxides.

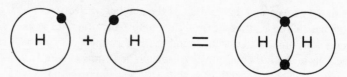

Fig. 1.6 Sharing of electrons in the hydrogen molecule
gives both a closed shell structure.

only one carbon atom per molecule. Carbon, with four electrons in the
L-shell, needs four more for a closed shell and in methane it obtains
them by sharing pairs of electrons with hydrogen atoms. Each of the
hydrogen atoms also achieves a closed shell structure just as in the
hydrogen molecule (Fig. 1.7).

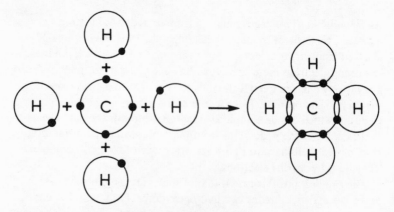

Fig. 1.7 Sharing of electrons between a carbon atom
and four hydrogen atoms in covalent bonding allows
all the atoms to have closed shell structures. This
diagram is purely schematic; the hydrogen atoms in
methane are not arranged in a square. (Ch. 4, p.60)

Water (H_2O) is formed from oxygen and hydrogen in much the same
way. In this case the oxygen atom requires two electrons to complete
the L-shell and obtains them by sharing with two hydrogen atoms
(Fig. 1.8).

In some cases, atoms share more than pairs of electrons, but the
number shared is almost always even (2, 4, or 6). In carbon dioxide

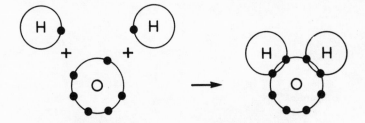

Fig. 1.8 Electron-sharing in the formation of the water molecule.

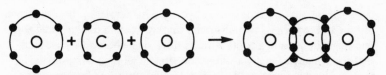

Fig. 1.9 Electron-sharing in the carbon dioxide molecule.

(CO_2), for example, the carbon atom shares four electrons with each oxygen atom, so that all three atoms are surrounded by the stable arrangement of eight electrons (Fig. 1.9). In the nitrogen molecule, containing two nitrogen atoms, each of the atoms reaches the closed shell structure by sharing six electrons.

It is convenient to represent a pair of electrons in a covalent bond by a single line between the symbols for the atoms. A bond with four or six electrons is similarly shown by a double or triple line, and such bonds are usually referred to as *double* or *triple* bonds. A bond formed by one pair of electrons only is called a *single bond*. The various covalent compounds we have discussed so far are illustrated in this way in Fig. 1.10. Such a representation of a molecule is often called a *structural formula*. It is schematic in that it does not show the actual arrangement of the atoms in space, but it does show which atoms are attached to which and by what kind of bond.

8. *Valency*

The number of single covalent bonds which an atom can form is a characteristic of that atom and is called its *valency*. From·the examples

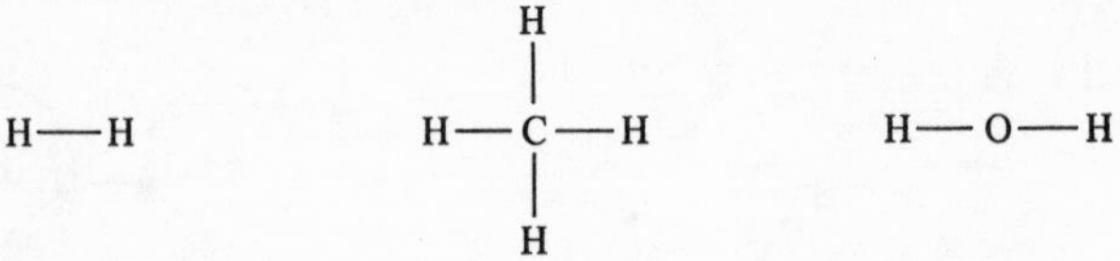

$$H\!-\!H$$

$$H\!-\!\overset{\displaystyle H}{\underset{\displaystyle H}{C}}\!-\!H$$

$$H\!-\!O\!-\!H$$

hydrogen   methane   water

$$O\!=\!C\!=\!O$$ $$N\!\equiv\!N$$

carbon dioxide   nitrogen

Fig. 1.10 Some structural formulae

in the last section we can see that hydrogen has a valency of one, carbon
of four and oxygen of two. Provided that we count a double bond as
two single bonds and a triple bond as three single bonds we shall find
that the valency of many atoms is the same in all their compounds. In
carbon dioxide, for example, carbon is still four valent (tetravalent) and
oxygen two valent (bivalent); in the nitrogen molecule (N_2), nitrogen is
three valent (trivalent).

The reason for this constancy of valency is that each single covalent
bond formed by an atom brings a share of one more electron to the
atom's outer shell, as you can readily see from the examples of the last
section. Since the valency of the atom is the number of single covalent
bonds that it can form this number is just equal to the number of
electrons needed to complete a closed shell structure. Atoms in Group
IV of the periodic table with four electrons needed for a closed shell
structure, have a valency of four (e.g. carbon); atoms in Group V with
three electrons needed, have a valency of three (e.g. nitrogen); Group
VI atoms have a valency of two and Group VII of one.

Knowledge of the valency of atoms makes it very easy to write
down the formulae of simple compounds. All that is needed is to
ensure that the total number of valencies of one kind of atom is the
same as the total number of valencies of the other. The simplest
compound of carbon and chlorine is a typical example. Carbon in
Group IV is four valent; chlorine in Group VII is univalent. Four
chlorine atoms, giving a total valency of four, will therefore combine
with one carbon atom to form a compound CCl_4 called carbon
tetrachloride. We could have reached this conclusion equally well, of

course, by means of the way we used when discussing CH_4, but the use of valency shortens the process considerably.

The valency concept can be extended also to ionic compounds. In simple ionic compounds such as sodium chloride (NaCl), one of the elements involved is always from the right hand side of the periodic table (chlorine in the case of NaCl), and one is from the left (sodium in the case of NaCl). We already know how to work out the valency of the right hand side element and we can use this valency, and the empirical formula of the compound to obtain a valency for the left hand side element. In the case of sodium chloride, chlorine has a valency of one, the empirical formula is NaCl. We have thus one atom of sodium to each each atom of chlorine and conclude that the valency of sodium must be one. The same result follows from the formula, Na_2O, for the oxide of sodium.

In fact we can see fairly easily that the valency of an element at the left hand side of the periodic table is equal to the number of electrons it must lose to reach a closed shell structure. When an ionic compound is formed, these electrons go to make up the outer shells of the element from the right hand side of the periodic table so that the two ways of working out the empirical formula – by the number of electrons transferred, or by the valencies of the atoms – are equivalent.

An extension of this terminology, which we shall use later, is to attribute to an ion a valency equal to its charge. Thus we call Na^+ a univalent ion and O^{2-} a divalent ion. One reason for doing this is that there are many ions which contain more than one atom, such as sulphate (SO_4^{2-}) or the biologically extremely important phosphate (PO_4^{3-}), and it is convenient to be able to apply the valency concept to them also.

Problem 1.4.   Using the concept of valency, work out the empirical formulae of sodium sulphate and calcium phosphate.

9. *Variable valency*

The foregoing discussion has implied that the valency of an element is always the same, but this is not strictly true. Some elements, such as carbon and oxygen, almost always have the same valency. Others, such as phosphorus or sulphur, can show different valencies in different

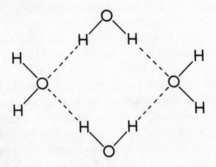

Fig. 1.11 Structural formula showing hydrogen bonding in water.

compounds. The very simplified account of bonding which we have given in this chapter is not really adequate to explain this — indeed it is not completely understood by chemists in all cases — but we mention it here in the hope of avoiding confusion in later chapters.

10. *The hydrogen bond*

One other kind of bonding which is rather different from the kinds of bond what we have discussed so far, is extremely important in biological systems. This is the so-called hydrogen bond. We cannot here attempt to explain its origin because it cannot be easily understood in terms of the concepts that we have introduced in this chapter; in fact, chemists still dispute its exact nature among themselves.

It occurs whenever a hydrogen atom covalently bonded to one of the atoms in the top right hand corner of the periodic table (e.g. nitrogen, oxygen, fluorine and, to a lesser extent, chlorine — the so-called electronegative atoms) comes close to another very electronegative atom. The hydrogen remains attached to the atom that it is bonded to, but is also, much more weakly, attracted to the other atom. The strength of a typical hydrogen bond is about one-sixteenth that of a covalent bond between, say, a carbon atom and a hydrogen atom. To emphasize this, hydrogen bonds are usually represented in structural formulae by a dotted line.

A common example of the hydrogen bond occurs in water. There are two hydrogen atoms in every molecule attached to the electronegative atom of oxygen, and these hydrogen atoms can, in liquid water or in ice, come close to the oxygen atoms of other water molecules, so that neighbouring water molecules are held together by hydrogen bonds (Fig. 1.11)

The two electronegative atoms involved in a hydrogen bond need not be identical. The hydrogen bonds that are of biological importance most commonly involve a hydrogen atom covalently bonded to nitrogen forming a hydrogen bond to oxygen.

CHAPTER 2

Energy and Equilibrium

1. *Kinds of energy*

Energy is the ability to do *work*. In order to understand this rather terse definition, we must first look briefly at the scientific use of the term 'work' which differs to some extent from its everyday use. Scientifically, work is said to be done when the place where a force acts moves through a distance in any direction other than at right angles to the direction of the force.

When you walk upstairs, for example, work is done – indeed you do it – because the force of gravity acts on you in a vertical direction and you move in a direction which is not at right angles to it. When you walk on a level surface, on the other hand, the direction of movement is at right angles to the direction of the gravitational force, and you don't do any work, at least as far as gravitational forces are concerned. However, the force involved need not be gravitational. If you squeeze a rubber ball or pull a pin off a magnet you do work. In the first case the force is the pressure that you apply to the ball (or, more correctly, the outward pressure that the ball exerts on your hand – the two are equal); in the case of the magnet the force is the attraction of the magnet for the pin.

Energy, then, is the ability to do this kind of work, and it can be found in many different forms. The simplest is *potential energy*, which is the energy which something possesses because of its state or position. Suppose you are sitting on the top end of a see-saw. Then you can do work by raising the person on the other end of the see-saw against the force of gravity. You have this energy because of your position – when you have done the work you will have lost your position at the top of the see-saw – and so the ability to do work in this case is potential energy.

Notice that when the work has been done, and you have lost your

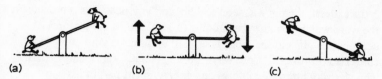

Fig. 2.1 (a) The girl at the top end of the see-saw has
potential energy because of her position.
(b) The energy is converted to kinetic energy,
(c) and back to potential energy – of the boy now.

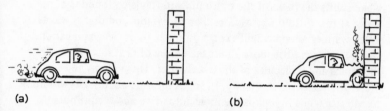

Fig. 2.2 (a) Kinetic energy
(b) can be made to do work.

potential energy, the person at the other end of the see-saw has been
lifted up and now has the potential energy instead; he can do work by
lifting you up again. This is an example of a very fundamental scientific
principle called either the *Law of Conservation of Energy*, or the *First
Law of Thermodynamics*. This law states that energy can neither be
created nor destroyed, but only converted from one form into another.
On the see-saw, for example, the potential energy of the person at one
end is converted into the potential energy of the person at the other
end as one goes down and the other up.

Kinetic energy is the energy which something possesses because it is
moving. If a car runs into a wall, the energy used in doing the work of
crushing the front of it comes from the kinetic energy of the car. If you
drop a ball the potential energy which it had when it was in your hand
is gradually converted into kinetic energy as it falls. The further the ball
falls, the more potential energy it loses and the more kinetic energy it
gains and so it falls faster.

Heat is also a form of energy, If, for example, you hold a drawing
pin by the stem and rub the head of it on a piece of fabric (your sleeve

is the easiest), the pin will soon feel hot to the touch. This is because
the work which you have been doing (against the frictional force
between the pin and the fabric) has used up some of your energy and
converted it into heat. Lord Rayleigh, the famous Victorian physicist
who was very interested in heat and energy, spent part of his
honeymoon in Switzerland with a thermometer measuring the
temperature at the tops and bottoms of waterfalls. When the water
falls over a waterfall, the potential energy which it has at the top is
converted first to kinetic energy as it falls, and then to heat energy
when it hits the rocks at the bottom. Lord Rayleigh found that the
water at the bottom was warmer than at the top, and that it was as
much warmer as one would expect on the basis of this explanation.

We can say a little more about the nature of heat if we go back to
the atoms and molecules of the last chapter. These atoms and
molecules are never stationary. In solids they are continually vibrating
to and fro, while in liquids the molecules move about continually,
rather like people in a closely packed, jostling crowd (which is why
liquids, like crowds, do not have a definite shape). Since the atoms and
molecules are moving, they possess kinetic energy, and it is this energy
that we call heat. If we put energy into something, the drawing pin
of the last paragraph for example, that energy is actually used to
increase the kinetic energy, and hence the speed of vibration of the
atoms of the pin. The more rapid movement of the atoms makes the
pin feel hotter.

A form of energy which is very important to plants is *radiant energy*,
more correctly called *electromagnetic radiation*. Radiant energy can
travel unchanged through air or empty space, and so can carry energy
from one body to another at a distance, independently of anything in
between. It can take various forms, of which radio waves, infra-red
radiation and light are the most familiar.

It is infra-red radiation which carries energy from, say, an electric
fire to its surroundings. You can detect this kind of radiation by holding
out your hand to the fire; you hand gets warm, so that it must have
received energy from somewhere, in fact by absorbing the infra-red
radiation given off by the fire. That ordinary visible light is a form of
energy is less easy to demonstrate. The amounts of light energy
commonly met with are very much smaller than the amounts of infra-red

energy given off by fires; we are only aware of them because our eyes are extremely sensitive detectors of light. Only extremely bright light carries enough energy to be detectable by its heating effect on the skin. Nevertheless, it is the light energy absorbed by green plants which is the ultimate source of almost all the energy which is available on the earth.

2. *Amounts of energy*

How is energy measured? What kinds of unit should we use to measure it? Since energy is the ability to do work, one way to measure it would be by the amount of work that it can do. First, then, we must look at the measurement of work and this in turn requires a unit for force. The unit of force is the *newton*. A force has a strength of one newton (1 N) if, when it acts on something weighing one kilogramme for one second, the speed of that thing is increased by one metre per second. The unit of work is the *joule*. If a force of one newton moves through one metre, one joule (1 J) of work is done. The unit for energy is identical. The amount of energy required to do one joule of work is called one joule also.

This probably all seems rather abstract. To make it a bit more realistic, let us consider some of our earlier examples. A 6-stone boy, 5 feet up in the air on a see-saw, has a potential energy of about 50 joules (50 J); a car weighing 15 cwt moving at 50 m.p.h. has a kinetic energy of about 28 000 kilojoules (28 000 kJ, 1 kJ = 1000 J); the amount of heat needed to heat a 3-pint kettle to the boiling point of water, is about 5350 J (5·35 kJ).

Another unit of energy that you may well meet is the *calorie* (cal). This unit was originally used for heat energy only, and is the amount of heat needed to heat one gramme of water by one degree centigrade. Numerically it is equal to 4·184 J. The kilocalorie (kcal), equal to 1000 cal, is also used, but neither of these units form part of the international system of units (Système Internationale, SI) which has gradually been adopted by scientists since its introduction in 1960. The only SI units of energy are the joule and its multiples (kJ etc.)

3. *Chemical energy*

There is one other form of energy which is very important in living systems — *chemical energy*. If you like, you can think of this as a kind of potential energy for it is energy which a body possesses because of the chemical state that its atoms are in. Suppose that in a chemical reaction the molecules of a substance were split up into their constituent atoms. Then work would have been done against the forces holding the atoms together and, in principle, that work could be recovered by letting the atoms combine again. The separated atoms, therefore, possess a kind of potential energy which is usually called chemical energy.

This idea can be extended to other kinds of reactions besides those in which atoms combine into molecules, the oxidation of glucose to carbon dioxide and water for example.

$$C_6H_{12}O_6 + 6O_2 = 6CO_2 + 6H_2O$$

If we could form the compounds on the left hand side of this equation directly from the atoms, that is, in molar quantities, making 1 mole of glucose from 6 moles of carbon atoms, 12 moles of hydrogen atoms and 6 moles of oxygen atoms, and making 6 moles of oxygen molecules from 12 moles of oxygen atoms, the amount of energy liberated as the bonds are formed would be 9729 kJ.* On the other hand if we could form the compounds on the right hand side, 6 moles of carbon dioxide and 6 moles of water from the same atoms, the amount of energy liberated would be 12 546 kJ. The various chemical bonds in CO_2 and water must therefore be stronger than those in glucose and oxygen by the difference of these quantities, 2817 kJ. It follows from the First Law of Thermodynamics that if the above reaction is carried out, 2817 kJ of energy will be liberated per mole of glucose oxidized. This quantity is called the *heat of reaction* (because the energy will appear as heat if glucose is actually burned in oxygen) and can be thought of as being stored up as chemical energy in the glucose molecule.

As we have already mentioned, all animals obtain most of their energy requirements by carrying out this reaction. However, glucose is

* This reaction cannot in fact be carried out directly, but the energy change can be calculated from the changes in other directly measurable reactions using the First Law of Thermodynamics.

not actually burned inside living organisms; instead they carry out the reaction in a finely controlled series of steps, which results in much of the energy appearing in forms, other than heat, which are useful to the organism.

Problem 2.1.   The energy of a moving motor-car derives originally from the sun. Through what forms has this energy probably passed?

4. *Conversion of energy from one form to another*

The First Law of Thermodynamics states that energy can only be converted from one form to another, but it says nothing about which conversions are possible. Kinetic energy can be completely converted into heat as in Lord Rayleigh's waterfalls, but heat cannot be completely converted into kinetic energy. If it could, we should be able to drive ships by taking heat energy out of the surrounding sea-water leaving a wake of colder water behind the ship, which seems intrinsically ridiculous; or heat in a ball, lying on the floor, might be converted to kinetic energy, causing the ball to get colder and jump up in the air. Such phenomena are never observed, and it is the impossibility of them, and others like them, which is asserted by the *Second Law of Thermodynamics*.

It would be beyond the scope of this book to give a formal statement of this law. Instead, we will go back to the molecular view of heat and see what light this throws on the question. What, on the molecular view, would happen if a ball used some of its heat energy to jump into the air? Initially, the energy in question would be the kinetic energy of the molecules in the ball moving about in an irregular chaotic way. When the whole ball started to move, all the molecules in it would be moving in the same direction. In other words this impossible phenomenon would amount to the random irregular motions of the molecules arranging themselves so that all the molecules were simultaneously moving in the same direction — a change from irregular, chaotic movement to regular, ordered movement.

Such a spontaneous change is contrary to all one's experience. All spontaneous changes occur in the opposite direction, from a regular, ordered situation, to an irregular, disordered one. Think about dropping

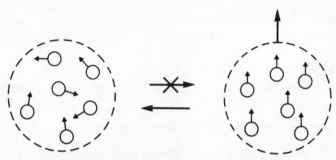

Fig. 2.3 The random motions of heat energy never change spontaneously to ordered motion. The reverse process is common.

an egg, or shuffling a pack of cards initially in suits, or leaving a small child alone in a room. The Second Law of Thermodynamics is a formal quantitative statement of these ideas.

It is often convenient in this connection to think about the *quality* of energy as well as its quantity. Energy of a highly ordered kind can be thought of as high quality energy which is degraded to lower quality energy in any spontaneous change. Heat in a body at a high temperature is thus higher quality energy than heat in a body at a low temperature, since heat flows spontaneously from a higher to a lower temperature. The chemical energy in glucose is high quality energy since it can be spontaneously degraded to heat when the glucose is burned. The kinetic energy of a body is high quality energy, and so on. Any spontaneous change leads to a degradation of energy and an increase in disorder.

An important apparent contradiction of this concept is the growth of living organisms. Living tissue is obviously a highly ordered form of matter, while the raw materials from which it is built, especially the carbon dioxide, water and mineral-salt solutions used by plants, are a good deal less ordered. How do living organisms contrive this apparently impossible change? The answer is that we must consider the overall changes taking place. It is a familiar idea that living organisms need energy in order to grow. The reason that they need this energy is in order to degrade it to heat, thus increasing the disorder of their surroundings (by increasing the kinetic energy of random movement of the molecules) by more than enough to compensate for the increasing order in the living organism itself. The energy that organisms need must therefore always be in a high quality form – chemical energy stored in food in the case of animals, radiant energy in the form of sunlight in the case of plants.

5. *Rates of chemical change*

We have seen that any spontaneous change is accompanied by an increase in disorder; indeed the tendency to increase disorder can be thought of as the driving force of any change, chemical or otherwise. We want now to look at the rate at which chemical changes occur. Chemical reactions can occur very rapidly, for example, the reaction between sodium and water mentioned in the last chapter, or the even more rapid reactions between acids and bases (Chapter 3) which are complete in a fraction of a second; or they can occur very slowly, for example, the reaction between iron and oxygen which we call rusting. Almost all the reactions that occur in living organisms occur with the various compounds involved dissolved in water (i.e. in aqueous solution) and so we will discuss only the factors which influence the rates of such reactions. Crudely, there are three factors involved: the energy required to make the reaction occur (the activation energy), the temperature, and the concentration of the reacting compounds (or reactants).

According to the simplest valid theory of chemical reactions, in order for two molecules to react, they must come together with at least a certain amount of kinetic energy; in other words, they must bump against each other hard enough to break the bonds which have to be broken to form the products of the reaction. We can now see how the three factors mentioned above influence the rate of reaction:

(i)   *The activation energy*. This is the measure of the hardness of bump needed. Bumps of all degrees of hardness are continually occuring in a solution as the molecules move about. If the activation energy of a reaction is not large, many of the bumps will be hard enough to make the reaction occur and so the reaction will take place rapidly. If the activation energy is large enough, few bumps will be hard enough to cause reaction and the rate will be low.

(ii)   *The temperature*. The higher the temperature, the faster the molecules move and the harder they bump, so that reactions occur

faster at higher temperatures. Twice the rate for a 10°C rise in temperature is a useful rough rule.

(iii) *The concentration of the reactants.* Concentration means the
amount of material in a particular volume and is usually measured in
moles per litre (mole l^{-1}). A solution containing one mole of substance
dissolved in one litre of water is said to be one *molar* (1 M). The
concentration of the reagents affects the frequency with which they
will bump together; the higher the concentration, i.e. the larger the
number of molecules in a given volume, the more frequent the bumps
and the faster the reaction. The symbol [X] is often used for the
concentration of substance X.

The relationships described in (i) and (ii) above cannot be expressed
in a very simple quantitative way, but the concentration dependence
can. This dependence is called the *law of mass action* and states that the
rate of a reaction is directly proportional to the concentration of the
reagents. For the reaction between an alcohol and an acid (Chapter 4)
this relation can be written

$$\text{rate of reaction} = k \times [\text{alcohol}] \times [\text{acid}]$$

where k is a constant called the *rate constant* and depends on the
temperature and the activation energy.

6. *Catalysis*

There is one other factor that can affect the rate of a reaction — the
presence of a *catalyst.* The classical definition of a catalyst is a substance
which changes the rate of a chemical reaction without itself taking part
in the reaction. Such a definition both sounds ludicrous and is. What a
catalyst almost invariably does is to react with one of the reagents in a
reaction and later to be liberated unchanged as one of the products of
the reaction. A single-step process is thus converted into a multistage
process and, in the case of a catalyst which increases the rate of a
reaction, each of the new steps will have a lower activation energy than
the uncatalysed reaction, thus causing the rate to increase.

Almost all reactions in biological systems involve catalysts, here
called *enzymes,* for most of the reactions have such high activation

energies in the absence of a catalyst that they could not occur at a useful rate at the temperature of a living organism. The compound whose reaction is catalysed by an enzyme is called the *substrate* of the enzyme. Enzymes are proteins which have an active site on the surface of the molecule where a substrate molecule can attach itself. This attached molecule can then react readily (with a low activation energy) forming products which are not attached to the enzyme and hence leave the enzyme molecule free to catalyse the reactions of another molecule of substrate. The rate of an enzymatically catalysed reaction is usually the rate at which the complex of enzyme and substrate is formed. By the law of mass action we can therefore write

$$\text{rate of reaction} = k \times [\text{substrate}] \times [\text{enzyme}].$$

A system which is easy to study experimentally is the decomposition of starch by the enzyme amylase. Here

$$\text{rate} = k \times [\text{starch}] \times [\text{amylase}].$$

As the starch is gradually used up during the reaction [starch] becomes smaller, and so does the rate of reaction, so that the amount of starch present falls rapidly at first and then more and more slowly, as shown

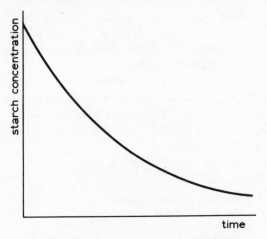

Fig 2.4 Variation of starch concentration with time

in Fig. 2.4. You ought to be able to deduce the effect on the rate of reaction of changing the temperature or the enzyme concentration. These effects are discussed in almost every biology text.

Problem 2.2   When 1 ml of amylase solution is added to 1 l of starch solution continaing 2 g l^{-1}, 5 mg of starch are hydrolysed in the first minute of the reaction. How much starch would you expect to be hydrolysed in the first minute if 2 ml of the amylase solution were added to 1 l of starch solution containing 6 g l^{-1}?

7. *Chemical equilibrium*

All chemical reactions can proceed either forwards, from reagents to products, or backwards, from products to reagents. If a mixture of compounds that can react is left to itself, therefore, products will start to form and these in turn will start to reform the reactants. If the reaction mixture is left long enough, the rates of the two reactions will become the same so that any given compound in the mixture will be reacting and being reformed at the same rate. The amounts present will not change with time, and chemical reaction, though continuing, will no longer be detectable. Such a system is said to be at *equilibrium*. In some cases such an equilibrium mixture will contain very little of the reactants, in which case the presence of the back reaction may be neglected. In other cases this is not so.

We can easily use the law of mass action to find out how the concentrations of the various compounds are related at equilibrium. As an example we will consider the equilibrium between hydrogen ions (H^+), hydroxide ions (OH^-) and water molecules (H_2O), reacting according to the equation

$$H_2O = H^+ + OH^-$$

The rate of the decomposition of water into ions (the forward reaction) is given by

$$\text{rate forward} = k_{\text{forward}} \times [H_2O]$$

The rate of the reaction between hydrogen and hydroxide ions (the back reaction) can be written

$$\text{rate back} = k_{back} \times [H^+] \times [OH^-]$$

At equilibrium these two rates are equal.

$$k_{back} \times [H^+] \times [OH^-] = k_{forward} \times [H_2O]$$

or
$$\frac{k_{forward}}{k_{back}} = \frac{[H^+][OH^-]}{[H_2O]}$$

The ratio of the two rate constants is called the *equilibrium constant (K)*

$$K = \frac{k_{forward}}{k_{back}} = \frac{[H^+][H^-]}{[H_2O]}$$

Since the rate constants depend only on the temperature (and the activation energies), K itself, for a particular reaction, will depend only on the temperature.

The numerical values of equilibrium constants vary enormously; in the example used above K is $1 \cdot 8 \times 10^{-16}$ mole litre^{-1}, and smaller ones are known. Equilbrium constants are always written so that the concentrations of the compounds on the right hand side of the equation appear in the numerator. Had we written the equation for the dissociation of water the other way round as

$$H^+ + OH^- = H_2O$$

the expression for the equilibrium constant would have been

$$K = \frac{[H_2O]}{[H^+][OH^-]}$$

and its value would of course have been the reciprocal of the value quoted above, $1/(1 \cdot 8 \times 10^{-16}) = 5 \cdot 5 \times 10^{15}$ litres mole^{-1}. The existence of very small equilibrium constants therefore implies the existence of very large ones.

All the equilibria of importance in biological systems occur in aqueous solution. Water therefore is always present in a very large quantity and its concentration is always effectively constant, since 1 l of solution will contain very close to 1 l of water. The density of water is 1 kg l^{-1}, and its molecular weight is 18 so that 1 l contains $1000/18 =$ 55·55 moles. In the expression for the equilibrium constant of a reaction involving water, therefore, we can always write

$$[H_2O] = 55·55$$

so that, for example, $[H^+] [OH^-] = 55·55K$ (a constant); it is conventional in such cases to call $55·55K$ the equilibrium constant and omit $[H_2O]$ in the definition of K. In the above example then, the equilibrium constant is usually written

$$K = [H^+] [OH^-]$$

with the value $55·55 \times 1·8 \times 10^{-16} = 10^{-14}$ mole^2 litre^{-2}.

Finally, we note that the presence of a catalyst does not affect the value of an equilibrium constant. This is not obvious from what has been said above, but can be rigorously proved by the use of the laws of thermodynamics. It follows that if a catalyst increases the rate of a forward reaction, it must increase the rate of the reverse reaction by the same factor.

Problem 2.3.   In the presence of acid, ethanol and acetic acid react partially to form ethyl acetate and water. If an equilibrium mixture of these compounds contains 0·4 moles of ethanol, 0·3 moles of acetic acid, and 0·6 moles of ethyl acetate, in 1 l of aqueous solution, what is the equilibrium constant for the reaction?

Introduction to Inorganic Chemistry

The majority of compounds found in living organisms are organic compounds, which is almost synonymous with compounds of carbon. However, there are a number of inorganic compounds which are biologically important, or which are frequently used in biological laboratories, and it is the chemistry of some of these which we shall consider in this chapter.

Many of the inorganic compounds with which the biologist is concerned are ionic in nature. The reactions of such compounds in aqueous solution can always be looked at in two ways. When an ionic compound is dissolved in water, the positive and negative ions (cations and anions) of which it is composed separate from one another to a greater or less extent and move about independently in the solution. Reactions in such a solution can therefore be looked upon as the reactions of either the constituent ions or the compounds from which they are derived. Both viewpoints have their advantage, and it is as well to keep both in mind.

1. *Oxygen and air*

Air is necessary for almost all living organisms. It is a mixture of several different colourless and odourless gases, mainly nitrogen (N_2) which forms about 78% of air, and oxygen (O_2) which forms about 21%. There is a small amount of the inert gas argon (about 1%) and traces of other inert gases, together with a small (0·03%) but very important quantity of carbon dioxide (CO_2). In addition, air usually contains a very variable amount (0–2%) of water vapour.

Nitrogen gas is very unreactive, mainly because of its very strong triple bond, and biologically it acts mainly as a diluent for the other gases. For animals the important constituent is oxygen, which is needed to combine with glucose and other food substances to yield supplies of energy. Oxygen is a very reactive gas which combines vigorously with a wide variety of other substances, expecially on heating. The ordinary burning of inflammable materials in air is, in fact, reaction with gaseous oxygen. The products of such reactions are usually simple compounds of oxygen and the various elements present in the inflammable material, as in the familiar combustion of glucose,

$$C_6H_{12}O_6 + 6O_2 = 6CO_2 + 6H_2O$$

2. Oxides

Such simple compounds are called oxides, and can be roughly divided into two classes according to whether the element combined with oxygen comes from the upper right and centre of the periodic table (e.g. carbon, phosphorus, sulphur) or from the left of the periodic table and the transition elements (e.g. sodium, magnesium, calcium, iron). It is convenient to refer to the first group of elements as *non-metals*, the second as *metals*.

As you may be able to predict from the discussion on valence in Chapter 1, the non-metal oxides are covalent while the metal oxides are ionic. This is reflected in their physical properties. The ionic metal oxides are held together throughout the solid by the strong forces between cations (positively charged ions) and anions (negatively charged ions). They are therefore solids at room temperature and are difficult to melt or boil since these processes require separating the ions from one another. Familiar examples are quicklime which is calcium oxide (CaO), and rust which is mainly iron oxide (Fe_2O_3).

The covalent non-metal oxides form discrete molecules which are much more weakly held together. They are therefore usually volatile (easily boiled) and often occur as gases. Of particular importance to us are the oxides of carbon (carbon dioxide, CO_2) and hydrogen (water, H_2O). Some others are mentioned in Table 3.1.

The metal and non-metal oxides are also different in their reactions with water. Many of the metal oxides are inert to water, but some of them (sodium, potassium, magnesium, calcium) dissolve. The cations are virtually unaffected by this process, merely surrounding themselves with loosely bound water molecules in place of the O^{2-} oxide ions. The oxide ions, on the other hand, combine with the water to form a new

TABLE 3.1

Some Oxides

Oxide	Formula	Physical form at ordinary temps.	Product of reaction with water
Metal oxides			
Sodium oxide	Na_2O*	involatile solid	sodium hydroxide (caustic soda) NaOH
Potassium oxide	K_2O*	involatile solid	potassium hydroxide (caustic potash) KOH
Magnesium oxide	MgO	involatile solid	magnesium hydroxide MgOH
Calcium oxide (quicklime)	CaO	involatile solid	calcium hydroxide (slaked lime) $Ca(OH)_2$
Ferrous oxide	FeO	involatile solid	insoluble
Ferric oxide	Fe_2O_3	involatile solid	insoluble
Non-metal oxides			
Carbon dioxide	CO_2	gas (solidifies at $-77°C$)	carbonic acid H_2CO_3
Sulphur trioxide	SO_3*	volatile solid	sulphuric acid H_2SO_4
Phosphorus pentoxide	P_2O_5	solid	phosphoric acid H_3PO_4
Water (Hydrogen oxide)	H_2O	liquid	

* These oxides cannot be made by burning the element in oxygen; a different oxide results from such a reaction.

anion, the hydroxide ion (OH⁻). In general we can write

$$O^{2-} + H_2O = 2OH^-$$

or, specifically, for example,

$$CaO + H_2O = Ca^{2+} + 2OH^-$$

The metal and hydroxide ions move about quite independently in the solution. In the absence of water, hydroxide ions can join with metal ions to form ionic solids called hydroxides which can be obtained, for example, by boiling off the water from the solution, or by adding minimal quantities of water to the oxides in the first place. The most familiar hydroxides are those of sodium (caustic soda, NaOH), potassium (caustic potash, KOH), and calcium (slaked lime, Ca(OH)₂). The slaking of quicklime by the addition of water to it is a typical example of this reaction:

$$CaO + H_2O = Ca(OH)_2$$

Almost all the non-metal oxides react with water. In this case, however, the products of the reaction are not hydroxides.

$$P_2O_5 + 3H_2O = H_3PO_4$$
$$\text{phosphoric acid}$$

$$CO_2 + H_2O = H_2CO_3$$
$$\text{carbonic acid}$$

They are typical acids.

Problem 3.1.   Write down chemical equations to show the effect of water on magnesium oxide and sulphur trioxide.

3. Acids and bases

An *acid* can be conveniently defined as a compound which can dissociate to produce hydrogen ions. In fact, rather few inorganic acids can be persuaded to exist in their undissociated form. Even when pure, they tend to be liquids containing at least some hydrogen ions. An obvious exception is hydrochloric acid (HCl) which, when pure, is a typical covalent gas. It dissolves easily in water, however, to form a solution which consists almost entirely of H⁺ and Cl⁻ ions and little or no undissociated HCl. Most of the common acids are oxyacids, that is, the products of their dissociation are hydrogen ions and anions

TABLE 3.2

Some Inorganic Acids

Acid	Formula	Dissociation products (ions)		Strength (sections 4 and 6)
Hydrochloric acid	HCl	H^+ + Cl^-	chloride	strong
Sulphuric acid	H_2SO_4	H^+ + HSO_4^-	bisulphate	strong
		$2H^+$ + SO_4^{2-}	sulphate	moderate
Nitric acid	HNO_3	H^+ + NO_3^-	nitrate	strong
Phosphoric acid	H_3PO_4	H^+ + $H_2PO_4^-$	dihydrogen phosphate	strong
		$2H^+$ + HPO_4^{2-}	hydrogen phosphate	weak
		$3H^+$ + PO_4^{3-}	phosphate	very weak
Carbonic acid	H_2CO_3	H^+ + HCO_3^-	bicarbonate	weak
		$2H^+$ + CO_3^{2-}	carbonate	very weak

containing a non-metal atom and several oxygen atoms. Some common and important examples are listed in Table 3.2.

Carbonic acid needs special consideration. Although compounds containing the carbonate and bicarbonate ions (CO_3^{2-} and HCO_3^-) are well-known and stable, it is doubtful if the free acid really exists. When an acid is added to a carbonate, carbon dioxide bubbles off as a gas. Undoubtedly, hydrogen ions from the acid react with carbonate and bicarbonate ions, but the resulting acid, it if exists at all, rapidly decomposes into carbon dioxide and water.

Phosphoric acid is very important in biological systems, because phosphate ions play many essential roles in the chemical processes of life. Part of its importance arises from the fact that two or more phosphate ions can *condense* together under suitable conditions to form polyphosphates.

$$^-O{-}\overset{\overset{\displaystyle O}{\|}}{\underset{\underset{\displaystyle OH}{|}}{P}}{-}OH \;+\; HO{-}\overset{\overset{\displaystyle O}{\|}}{\underset{\underset{\displaystyle OH}{|}}{P}}{-}O^- \;=\; {}^-O{-}\overset{\overset{\displaystyle O}{\|}}{\underset{\underset{\displaystyle OH}{|}}{P}}{-}O{-}\overset{\overset{\displaystyle O}{\|}}{\underset{\underset{\displaystyle OH}{|}}{P}}{-}O^- \;+\; H_2O$$

The ion containing two phosphate groups is called pyrophosphate. Larger groupings of condensed phosphate ions are also well-known, but they have no special names. Other oxyacids share this property with phosphoric acid, but their *polyanions* are of no biological interest.

Bases are compounds which can react with hydrogen ions. Since the hydrogen ion has no electrons, if it is to react and form a covalent bond with some other compound, both the electrons for the bond must come from the other reactant. Bases, therefore, contain at least two unshared electrons. The commonest ones are the oxide ion O^{2-} which has none of its outer electrons shared, and the hydroxide ion OH^- where the oxygen atom has only two of its outer electrons shared. The product of the reaction of either of these ions with H^+ is water.

$$O^{2-} + 2H^+ = H_2O \qquad\qquad 3.1a$$

$$OH^- + H^+ = H_2O \qquad\qquad 3.1b$$

By extension, the word base is also applied to compounds containing O^{2-} or OH^- ions. Thus sodium hydroxide or iron oxide, for example, are often called bases. A base in this sense which is soluble in water is called an *alkali*. Notice also that the anion produced by the dissociation of an acid can be thought of as a base.

Of course, hydrogen ions or basic ions cannot exist by themselves. Hydrogen ions are produced from acids together with anions, and O^{2-} or OH^- ions are always associated with metal cations. The reactions in equations 3.1 therefore, are actually brought about by reacting acids with metal oxides or hydroxides; the equations can equally well be written to show this. For example, the reaction between sodium hydroxide and nitric acid could be written

$$NaOH + HNO_3 = NaNO_3 + H_2O$$

or $\qquad Na^+ + OH^- + H^+ + NO_3^- = Na^+ + NO_3^- + H_2O$

The product of such a reaction, an ionic compound made up of metal cations and acid anions is called a *salt*. Salts are named by the name of the metal followed by the name of the anion. $NaNO_3$, for example, is sodium nitrate. All salts of interest to us, if they are soluble in water, dissociate completely into ions in aqueous solution.

One important base which does not contain oxygen is ammonia, a compound of nitrogen and hydrogen (NH_3). Ammonia is a colourless gas with a pungent smell and is very soluble in water. It is this solution which is sold as household ammonia. Ammonia reacts with hydrogen ions to form the ammonium ion (NH_4^+).

$$NH_3 + H^+ = NH_4^+$$

NH_4^+ behaves in many respects like a metal ion and compounds containing NH_4^+ and an acid ion are referred to as ammonium salts.

Salts can also be produced by reacting a metal oxide or hydroxide directly with a non-metal oxide. This is particularly important in the case of carbonates which result from the reaction of bases with carbon dioxide.

$$2NaOH + CO_2 = Na_2CO_3 + H_2O$$

or $$Ca(OH)_2 + CO_2 = CaCO_3 + H_2O$$

Soda-lime, which is a mixture of $NaOH$ and CaO, removes CO_2 very effectively from gases passed over it, by means of this kind of reaction – a fact which is frequently used in respiration experiments. The lime-water test for CO_2 also depends on this reaction. Calcium hydroxide is moderately soluble in water, lime-water being the common name for this solution. Calcium carbonate, on the other hand, is insoluble in water, so that when gases containing carbon dioxide are bubbled through lime-water and the reaction of the second equation above takes place, insoluble white calcium carbonate is formed as a precipitate and the lime-water 'turns milky'.

4. *Strong and weak electrolytes–pH*

Compounds which produce ions in solution are called *electrolytes* (because the electrically charged ions can carry an electric current through the solution). If the compound exists in solution entirely in the form of ions, it is called a strong electrolyte. All salts mentioned in this book are strong electrolytes. Some electrolytes, however, particularly among acids and bases, are very little dissociated in aqueous solution. Such compounds are called weak electrolytes. There are also electrolytes of intermediate strength which partially dissociate.

The idea of chemical equilibrium presented in Chapter 2 can be applied to such compounds. If we represent a weak electrolyte by MA, dissociating according to the equation

$$MA = M^+ + A^-$$

the equilibrium constant for the reaction is

$$K = \frac{[M^+] \, [A^-]}{[MA]}$$

In this case the constant K is usually called the *dissociation constant*. Reactions of this kind are always very rapid, so that in any weak electrolyte solution the concentrations of the various species are related by this equation.

Of particular importance in biological systems are the equilibria involving hydrogen ions. If we have a solution containing a weak acid (HA, say) we can write

$$HA = H^+ + A^-$$

and
$$K = \frac{[H^+] \, [A^-]}{[HA]}$$

The ratio of the undissociated to the dissociated form of the acid therefore depends on the concentration of hydrogen ions

$$\frac{[HA]}{[A^-]} = K[H^+]$$

with similar reactions in the case of a base. Almost all the compounds found in living tissues, especially proteins, contain weakly acidic and basic groups, and the properties of the compounds depend critically on whether these compounds are in dissociated or undissociated form. The hydrogen ion concentration of solutions is thus of great importance in biology.

Hydrogen ion concentrations are not usually quoted directly.

Instead, a quantity called the pH is used, which is defined by the realtionship

$$pH = -\log_{10}[H^+]$$

For example, if a solution contains hydrogen ions at a concentration of 10^{-4} mole l^{-1},

$$pH = -\log_{10} 10^{-4} = -(-4) = 4 \qquad 3.2$$

In Chapter 2 we mentioned the dissociation of water

$$H_2O = H^+ + OH^-$$

and gave the value of the equilibrium constant as

$$K = [H^+][OH^-] = 10^{-14} \qquad 3.3$$

In pure water the H^+ and OH^- concentrations must be the same since each water molecule that dissociates produces one of each, so that the hydrogen ion concentration must be 10^{-7}. The pH of pure water is therefore 7. Addition of acids to pure water will increase the hydrogen ion concentration and so decrease the pH (equation 3.2 above, for example) so that acid solutions have a pH of less than 7. If alkaline solutions are added to water, the concentration of OH^- ions will increase and so, since the product must remain constant (equation 3.3 above), the concentration of H^+ ions will decrease, leading to pH values greater than 7. Some features of the pH scale are indicated in Fig. 3.1.

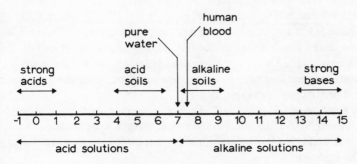

Fig. 3.1 Some features of the pH scale.

Problem 3.2.   Calculate the effect on the pH of adding 1 drop (say 0·05 ml) of bench HCl solution (2M concentration) to some pure water.

5. Buffer solutions

Problem 3.2 shows that the addition of a very small amount of acid to water produces a large pH change. Biological molecules are sensitive to changes of pH. It is therefore necessary that some method of stabilizing pH be found. The same method is used both by the scientist in the laboratory and by living organisms; it is to use a solution containing a weak acid and a salt of that acid.

Representing the acid by HA we have that

$$K = \frac{[H^+][A^-]}{[HA]}$$

or
$$[H^+] = K[HA]/[A^-]$$

Since HA is a weak acid, it is very little dissociated and HA can be taken as the concentration of the acid. The salt, on the other hand, will be a strong electrolyte and completely dissociated into metal ions and A^- ions, so that A^- can be taken as the concentration of the salt.

$$[H^+] = K[acid]/[salt]$$

or
$$pH = -\log_{10}[H^+] = -\log_{10}(K[acid]/[salt]) \qquad 3.4$$
$$= -\log_{10}K + \log_{10}([salt]/[acid])$$

Let us now see what the effect of adding a small quantity of H^+ ions to this solution is. The solution will now contain H^+ ions and A^- ions, and since HA is a weak acid, these will combine together for form more undissociated HA. In other words, the addition of a small amount of H^+ increases [acid] a little and decreases [salt] a little. If these concentrations were initially large however, their ratio and hence the pH would be virtually unchanged.

A solution of this kind is called a *buffer solution*, since the acid and salt present 'buffer' the solution against pH changes. In biological systems, carbonate and bicarbonate ions are important buffering species according to the equation

$$HCO_3^- = H^+ + CO_3^{2-}$$

Problem 3.3.   A buffer solution contains equal concentrations of acetic acid and sodium acetate. The dissociation constant of acetic acid is 1.9×10^{-5}. What is the pH of the buffer solution?

6. *Polybasic acids*

The number of hydrogen ions that can be formed from a single molecule of an acid is called its *basicity*. HCl, which can form one H^+ ion per molecule, is thus monobasic, H_2SO_4 is dibasic, and H_3PO_4 is tribasic. In general, the successive hydrogen ions can be removed only with more and more difficulty. For example, as far as its first hydrogen ion is concerned, H_2SO_4 is strong acid; no undissociated H_2SO_4 exists in aqueous solution. However the resulting bisulphate ion HSO_4^- is not such a strong acid and is not completely dissociated in aqueous solution. Sulphuric acid solutions, therefore, contain the ions H^+, HSO_4^- and SO_4^{2-} in varying proportions which depend on the pH. The ease with which successive dissociations can occur is indicated in the last two columns of Table 3.2.

7. *Oxidation and reduction*

A large number of the reactions which occur in biological systems are oxidations or reductions. We discuss such reactions in this chapter because the concepts of oxidation and reduction can be understood more easily in the context of inorganic chemistry.

Oxidation can be defined in a variety of ways. Although the various definitions are equivalent, it is useful to be familiar with several of them, because different reactions can often be most easily understood in terms of different definitions.

The simplest definition of all is that oxidation involves the addition of oxygen to a compound. The formation of CO_2 by burning of carbon in oxygen or air is a good example, as is the combustion of glucose. The carbon or glucose is said to be oxidized by the oxygen which is the *oxidizing agent* here. Ammonia will also burn in oxygen if the conditions are adjusted carefully and it would appear that this reaction ought also to be called an oxidation.

$$4NH_3 + 3O_2 = 2N_2 + 6H_2O$$

What has happened to the ammonia, though, is that hydrogen has been removed from it. In organic chemistry, the action of an oxidizing agent on a compound is very often the removal of hydrogen; so the definition of oxidation is extended to include the removal of hydrogen from a substance.

In the table of oxides (Table 3.1) two oxides of iron are listed: ferrous oxide (FeO), and ferric oxide (Fe_2O_3). In these oxides the iron atoms are present as divalent ferrous ions (Fe^{2+}) and trivalent ferric ions (Fe^{3+}) respectively. Corresponding chlorides can be obtained by dissolving the oxides in hydrochloric acid. Ferrous chloride can be converted to ferric chloride by the action of chlorine gas; ferrous oxide can be easily oxidized to ferric oxide by gaseous oxygen. These reactions are illustrated diagrammatically below

Reaction I is certainly an oxidation. It therefore seems consistent to call reaction II an oxidation also and this can be done by extending the definition to include the addition of any non-metallic element (except hydrogen) to a compound instead of just the addition of oxygen.

The relation between reactions I and II can be revealed more clearly, though, by thinking in terms of ions. No change takes place in the oxide or chloride ions of the FeO or $FeCl_2$ when the oxidation takes place, but the Fe^{2+} ions are converted to Fe^{3+} ions. In other words, an electron is removed from each Fe^{2+} ion leaving a more highly charged Fe^{3+} ion. We therefore arrive at a final definition of oxidation — the removal of electrons from an ion or compound.

Reduction is the opposite of oxidation and can be defined by reversing any of the definitions which we have given.

Oxidation	Reduction
Addition of oxygen or other non-metal atoms	Removal of oxygen or other non-metal atoms
Removal of hydrogen atoms	Addition of hydrogen atoms
Removal of electrons	Addition of electrons

Oxidation can never occur without a simultaneous reduction, for if an oxidizing agent oxidizes something, the oxidizing agent is itself reduced. In the oxidation of ammonia, for example, the ammonia is oxidized to nitrogen (removal of hydrogen atoms) while the oxygen is reduced to water (addition of hydrogen atoms). If we are prepared to think of ammonia (in a purely formal way) as made up of H^+ ions and an N^{3-} ion, and of water (again formally) as made up of H^+ ions and an O^{2-} ion, this reaction also can be interpreted in terms of the gain and loss of electrons. The hydrogen is present as H^+ ions throughout, so we can concentrate on the nitrogen and oxygen.

$$4N^{3-} + 3O_2 = 2N_2 + 6O^{2-}$$

The nitrogen has lost electrons (been oxidized) while the oxygen has gained electrons (been reduced). It must be emphasized that this is a purely *formal* way of looking at this reaction to show the relationship between the various definitions of oxidation and reduction. Ammonia and water are certainly not ionic compounds.

TABLE 3.3

Some Commonly Used Oxidizing and Reducing Agents

Oxidizing agents	Reducing agents
Oxygen gas	Hydrogen gas
Chlorine gas	Zinc metal
Potassium permanganate ($KMnO_4$)	Zinc amalgum (a solution of zinc in mercury)
Potassium dichromate ($K_2Cr_2O_7$)	

In Table 3.3 are listed some of the common oxidizing and reducing agents. It should be stressed, however, that these are only relative terms.

Hydrogen gas is a typical reducing agent (it will reduce heated copper oxide to the free metal, for example, being oxidized to water in the process,

$$CuO + H_2 = Cu + H_2O)$$

yet water can be reduced to hydrogen gas by the more powerful reducing agent, metallic calcium.

$$Ca + 2H_2O = Ca(OH)_2 + H_2$$

Problem 3.4.   Which of the following reactions can be looked on as oxidation-reduction reactions? What is being oxidized and what reduced?

   (a) $Mg + 2HCl = MgCl_2 + H_2$
   (b) $Ca + H_2 = CaH_2$
   (c) $CaO + 2HCl = CaCl_2 + H_2O$
   (d) $CaH_2 + 2H_2O = Ca(OH)_2 + 2H_2$

   (Note: CaH_2 is an ionic compound containing Ca^{2+} and H^- ions.)

CHAPTER 4

Introduction to Organic Chemistry

1. *Introduction*

Almost all the chemical compounds found in living organisms are compounds of carbon. As a result of this, the chemistry of *carbon compounds* — with a few exceptions such as carbon dioxide and the carbonates — has come to be treated apart from the rest of chemistry and to be called organic chemistry.

Carbon is unique among the elements in the extent to which it forms compounds in which large numbers of identical atoms are bonded together. This is perhaps the reason that carbon compounds form the basis of life, for these chains of carbon atoms form frameworks from which an almost infinite variety of molecules with widely varying properties can be constructed.

In organic chemistry then, we are not usually concerned with the properties of molecules as a whole, but rather with the properties of small groups of atoms, usually called *functional groups,* which form part of a molecule. For this reason we shall not usually use the empirical formulae that list the various atoms present in a molecule; instead we shall use structural formulae almost exclusively, either in full, or in a shorthand form which we shall gradually develop.

2. *Hydrocarbons*

Hydrocarbons are compounds of carbon and hydrogen only. They occur rather rarely in living organisms, but are of interest as typifying the carbon frameworks mentioned in the last section. Structural formulae for a number of hydrocarbons appear in Table 4.1.

The simplest possible hydrocarbon is methane, usually written CH_4 since there is no ambiguity in its structure as each of the four carbon valencies is used to attach a hydrogen atom. More complicated

TABLE 4.1

Some Hydrocarbons

Name	*Structural formula*	*Shorthand structural formula*
Methane	$H-\overset{\displaystyle H}{\underset{\displaystyle H}{C}}-H$	CH_4
Ethane	$H-\overset{\displaystyle H}{\underset{\displaystyle H}{C}}-\overset{\displaystyle H}{\underset{\displaystyle H}{C}}-H$	$CH_3 \cdot CH_3$
Propane	$H-\overset{\displaystyle H}{\underset{\displaystyle H}{C}}-\overset{\displaystyle H}{\underset{\displaystyle H}{C}}-\overset{\displaystyle H}{\underset{\displaystyle H}{C}}-H$	$CH_3 \cdot CH_2 \cdot CH_3$
Isobutane	$H-\overset{\displaystyle H}{\underset{\displaystyle H}{C}}-\overset{\displaystyle H}{\underset{\displaystyle \underset{\displaystyle H-\overset{H}{\underset{H}{C}}-H}{}}{C}}-\overset{\displaystyle H}{\underset{\displaystyle H}{C}}-H$	$\begin{array}{c} CH_3 \\ \searrow \\ CH \cdot CH_3 \text{ or } CH_3 \cdot CH(CH_3) \cdot CH_3 \\ \nearrow \\ CH_3 \end{array}$

hydrocarbons can be built up by forming *chains* of carbon atoms, straight or branched, and by satisfying with hydrogen atoms the valencies of each carbon atom which were not used up in forming bonds to other carbon atoms. A number of examples appear in Table 4.1.

The shorthand structural formulae in the third column of this table are built up by considering each carbon atom of the longest chain in the molecule in turn, and writing down the symbols for the other atoms attached to it, followed by a dot before the next carbon atom. A group of atoms attached to one bond of a carbon atom is surrounded by parentheses. Various intermediate simplifications can also be used, as used for isobutane, for example.

Hydrocarbons are characterized by their chemical stability. The bond between a hydrogen atom and a carbon atom attached to other carbon or hydrogen atoms only, is not easily broken; nor is a bond between two such carbon atoms. Hydrocarbons will burn if heated in air or oxygen, the products being carbon dioxide and water, but that almost completes their chemistry. Consequently, those parts of more complex organic molecules which consist of parts of a hydrocarbon molecule, can be treated as an inert framework for many purposes. Most liquid fuels (petrol, paraffin, diesel oil, etc.) are mixtures of various hydrocarbons.

The groupings derived from methane and ethane by the removal of one H atom occur especially frequently in other molecules. They are called the *methyl* (CH_3) and *ethyl* ($CH_3 \cdot CH_2 \cdot$ or C_2H_5) groups.

The hydrocarbons we have considered so far are called *saturated*. There are also hydrocarbons containing multiple bonds between carbon atoms; these are referred to as *unsaturated*. If the multiple bonds are double, the compounds are called *olefins*; triple-bonded compounds, *acetylenes*, are not important biologically.

The *olefin grouping* ($-CH = CH-$) is probably best looked on as a functional group, because it is very reactive compared to the single carbon—carbon bonds found in saturated hydrocarbons. Its typical reactions are addition reactions in which, formally, one of the carbon—carbon bonds is broken and an atom or group of atoms is attached to each of the free valencies so formed.* In biological systems the compound most commonly added is water, a hydrogen atom attaching itself at one end and the remaining OH group at the other, thus forming an alcohol (see the following section).

$$-CH = CH- \quad + \quad H-OH \quad = \quad -CH_2 - CHOH-$$

This reaction does not occur spontaneously on the absence of a catalyst. Bromine (Br_2) however, does add rapidly to olefins, without a catalyst, to give a dibromide.

$$-CH = CH- \quad + \quad Br_2 \quad = \quad -CH_2Br - CH_2Br-$$

* This is only a formal description of the process. The detailed mechanism of the actual reactions is rather different.

Bromine is brown and the dibromide is colourless; this provides a quick way of detecting olefinic groupings.

3. *The hydroxyl group – alcohols*

The next functional group we shall consider is the *hydroxyl group* (—OH). Oxygen being divalent, there is one bond left over for the group to attach itself to a carbon atom of a hydrocarbon framework. Some simple molecules of biological interest containing OH groups are listed in Table 4.2; such compounds are called *alcohols*. The OH group is not usually enclosed in parentheses in shorthand structural formulae.

Alcohols are quite different from inorganic hydroxyl compounds; they are neither acids nor bases. Although they will react with some acids to give compounds that are formally similar to salts, these reactions are slow and the resulting compounds, called *esters*, are not ionic compounds

TABLE 4.2

Some Alcohols

Name	Alternative names	Structural formula	Shorthand structural formula
Methanol	Methyl alcohol	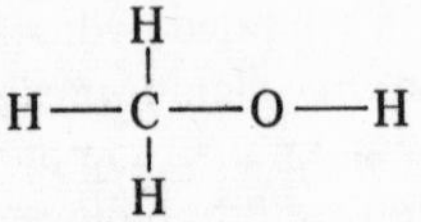 (structure)	CH_3OH
Ethanol	Ethyl alcohol 'Alcohol'	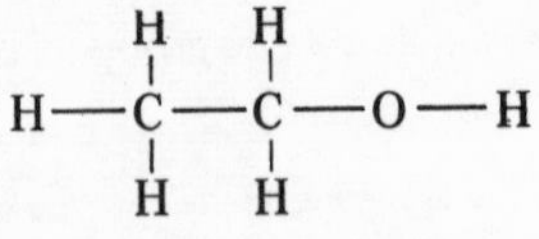 (structure)	$CH_3 \cdot CH_2OH$ or C_2H_5OH
Glycerol	Propan 1, 2, 3 tri-ol	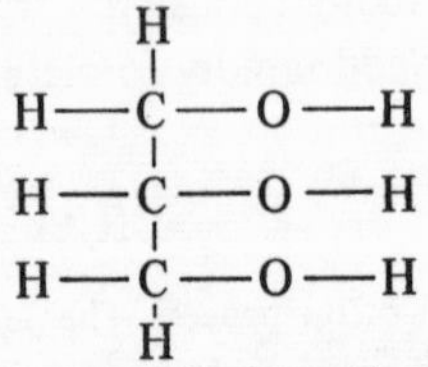 (structure)	$CH_2OH \cdot CHOH \cdot CH_2OH$

as salts are; for example

$$CH_3OH + H_2SO_4 = CH_3HSO_4 + H_2O$$

methyl hydro-
gen sulphate
(an ester)

The formation of phosphate esters, though not by direct reaction with phosphoric acid, is a very common reaction of alcohols in biochemistry.

The behaviour of alcohols on oxidation depends on how many hydrogen atoms are attached to the same carbon atom as the OH group. Oxidation involves the removal of one of these hydrogens together with the hydrogen of the OH group to give a compound containing a $C = O$ group (see section 4.4). If there are two hydrogens attached to the same carbon atom as the OH group, one of these will remain on oxidation and the product is called an aldehyde, for example

$$CH_3 \cdot CH_2OH \xrightarrow{\text{oxidation}} CH_3 \cdot C \overset{O}{\underset{H}{=}}$$

acetaldehyde
(an aldehyde)

If there is one such hydrogen the product is a ketone; for example

$$\overset{CH_3}{\underset{CH_3}{>}}CHOH \xrightarrow{\text{oxidation}} \overset{CH_3}{\underset{CH_3}{>}}C = O$$

acetone
(a ketone)

while if there is no such hydrogen the alcohol cannot easily be oxidized.

$$\overset{CH_3}{\underset{CH_3}{\overset{|}{-}}}COH \xrightarrow[\text{oxidized}]{\text{not easily}}$$

These oxidations can be carried out by any standard oxidizing agent, such as potassium permanganate; in living tissue the oxidizing agent is usually a nucleotide (Chapter 5) together with an enzyme catalyst.

The other main reaction of alcohols which is of biological importance, is dehydration to an olefin.

$$—CH_2 — CHOH — = —CH=CH— + H_2O$$

Again, this reaction can be carried out in the laboratory (using aluminium oxide as a catalyst) but higher temperatures are required than are needed by the enzyme catalysts of living tissue.

4. *The carbonyl group – aldehydes and ketones*

The functional group consisting of an oxygen atom doubly bonded to carbon ($>C=O$) is called the *carbonyl group*. The compounds in which it occurs are called *aldehydes* or *ketones* according to whether the carbonyl group is at the end of, or in the middle of, a carbon chain. Some typical examples of the two kinds are given in Table 4.3, which also shows the way in which they are represented in shorthand formulae.

TABLE 4.3

Some Carbonyl Compounds

Name	Structural formula	Shorthand formula
Aldehydes		
Formaldehyde	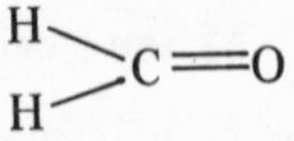	HCHO or CH_2O
Acetaldehyde	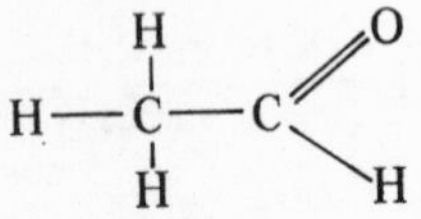	$CH_3 \cdot CHO$
Ketone		
Acetone	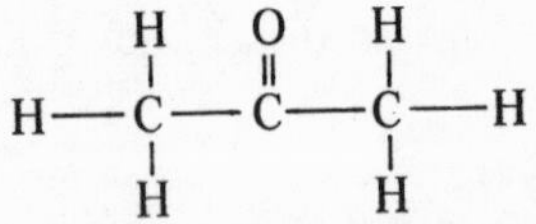	$CH_3 \cdot CO \cdot CH_3$ or $(CH_3)_2CO$

Since the carbonyl group, like the olefin group, contains a double bond, it might be expected that it would also undergo addition reactions. This is in fact the case, but rather few reactions of this kind are important biologically. Reduction back to an alcohol is such a reaction; in this, a hydrogen atom is added (by a reducing agent) to each end of the double bond.

$$\text{>C} = \text{O} + 2\text{H} = \text{>C} \big\langle {}^{\text{OH}}_{\text{H}}$$

Some compounds containing an activated C —H bond (see below) will also add to carbonyl compounds, an important reaction used to build up carbon chains in biological systems.

$$\text{>C} = \text{O} + \text{H} - \text{C} \leqslant = \text{>C} \big\langle {}^{\text{OH}}_{\text{C} \leqslant}$$

Some compounds containing OH groups, such as water or alcohols, will also add to C $=$ O bonds,

$$\text{>C} = \text{O} + \text{H} - \text{OR} = \text{>C} \big\langle {}^{\text{OH}}_{\text{OR}}$$

but the resulting compounds, except in a few special cases, are rather unstable, tending to revert to the carbonyl and hydroxyl compounds from which they were formed. In fact, compounds in which two oxygen atoms are singly bound to the same carbon atom are usually rather unstable, particularly if one of the oxygens forms part of an OH group.

Biologically, the main function of the carbonyl group seems to be its activating effect on adjacent atoms and groups. A simple example is found in the aldehydes which are easily oxidized to acids (next section); for example

$$\text{CH}_3\text{C} \big\langle {}^{\text{H}}_{\text{O}} \xrightarrow{\text{oxidation}} \text{CH}_3\text{C} \big\langle {}^{\text{OH}}_{\text{O}}$$

acetic acid

So easily are aldehydes oxidized that they are in fact quite strong reducing agents. They will, for example, reduce suitable solutions of cupric salts (such as Fehling's solution) to cuprous oxide, which appears as a reddish precipitate. Hydrocarbons, on the other hand, have no reducing properties so that the C — H bond must be affected by the neighbouring carbonyl group. Such activation is also necessary before a C—H grouping can add to another carbonyl group, as we have already mentioned.

6. *Carboxylic acids*

The functional group $-C\diagdown{}^{O}_{OH}$ (or $-COOH$) which contains both a
carboxyl and a hydroxyl grouping is called the *carboxyl group*. Its
most obvious property is that the hydrogen of the OH group is readily
lost as a hydrogen ion, leaving a negatively charged grouping behind it.

$$-C\diagdown{}^{O}_{OH} \ = \ -C\diagdown{}^{O}_{O^-} \ + \ H^+$$

Compounds containing this group, therefore, are *acids*, though usually
weak ones. The commonest example is acetic acid ($CH_3 \cdot COOH$); a
number of others are listed in Table 4.4. In biological systems the pH is
usually high enough for the dissociation of most carboxyl groups to be
essentially complete; so such groupings are usually present in their
ionized form.

The carbonyl group in a carboxylic acid is less reactive than in
aldehydes and ketones. It does not undergo addition reactions except
under rather specialized conditions, but it retains at least some of its
activating effect. Indeed, it is the activation of the neighbouring
hydroxyl group which leads to the acidic properties of carboxyl groups.

Biologically, the most important reaction of carboxyl compounds,
apart from their behaviour as acids, is loss of carbon dioxide to form a
compound containing one fewer carbon atoms. This reaction, referred
to as *decarboxylation*, normally requires that the carboxyl group be
activated by the presence of another neighbouring carboxyl group. For
example the reaction

$$CH_3 \cdot CO \cdot CH_2 \cdot COOH \ = \ CH_3 \cdot CO \cdot CH_3 \ + \ CO_2$$

will occur spontaneously on warming the acid. The carbon dioxide
produced in respiration arises from reactions of this kind.

6. *Amines and amides*

A compound which can be thought of as derived from ammonia (NH_3)
by the replacement of one or more hydrogen atoms by hydrocarbon
chains, is called an *amine*, for example, methylamine (CH_3NH_2). You
will remember from Chapter 3 that ammonia is a base, which combines

with hydrogen ions to form the ammonium ion.

$$NH_3 + H^+ = NH_4^+$$

Amines posses the same property even more markedly; they will combine with hydrogen ions more strongly than ammonia

$$-NH_2 + H^+ = -NH_3^+$$

and, especially in the case of amines in which all the hydrogen atoms have been replaced, are quite strong bases. Simple amines hardly occur biologically, but most basic compounds of biological origin contain $-NH_2$ groupings somewhere in the molecule.

Amides bear the same relationship to amines that carboxylic acids do to alcohols. They are compounds with an $-NH_2$ group (or an $-NH-$ or $-N=$ group) directly attached to a carbonyl group and are named from the acid from which they can be considered to be derived;

TABLE 4.4
Some Carboxylic Acids

Name	Shorthand formula	Ion
Formic acid	$H \cdot COOH$	$HCOO^-$ formate
Acetic acid	$CH_3 \cdot COOH$	CH_3COO^- acetate
Oxalic acid	$\begin{array}{c} COOH \\ \mid \\ COOH \end{array}$	$\begin{array}{c} COO^- \\ \mid \\ COO^- \end{array}$ oxalate
Succinic acid	$\begin{array}{c} \diagup COOH \\ CH_2 \\ \mid \\ CH_2 \\ \diagdown COOH \end{array}$	$\begin{array}{c} CH_2 \cdot COO^- \\ \mid \\ CH_2 \cdot COO^- \end{array}$ succinate
Stearic acid	$CH_3(CH_2)_{16}COOH^*$	$CH_3(CH_2)_{16}COO^-$ stearate
Carbonic acid	$O=C \diagup_{OH}^{OH}$	$O=C \diagup_{O^-}^{OH}$ bicarbonate $\quad O-C \diagup_{O^-}^{O^-}$ carbonate

* The symbol $(CH_2)_{16}$ indicates a chain of sixteen $-CH_2-$ groups.

for example

$$CH_3-C{\overset{O}{\underset{NH_2}{\lessgtr}}}$$

acetamide

$$CH_3-C{\overset{O}{\underset{NH-CH_3}{\lessgtr}}}$$

methyl acetamide
(a substituted amide)

The amide of carbonic acid $O=C{\overset{NH_2}{\underset{NH_2}{\lessgtr}}}$ is usually called urea.

As in the case of the carboxyl group, the $>\!C=\!O$ and the $-\!NH_2$ groups modify each other's properties. The effect on the carbonyl group is much the same as in an acid; it is not so reactive, but it retains its activating effects. The $-\!NH_2$ group is less basic than in an amine; in fact, amides are not usually thought of as bases. In addition, the $C-\!N$ bond is considerably weaker than in an amine. Simple amines are unaffected by boiling with acids or alkalis (apart from being converted to salts in the case of acids); amides are broken down (hydrolysed) at the $C-\!N$ bond to form the free acid and an amine or ammonia; for example

$$CH_3 \cdot CO \cdot NH_2 + NaOH = CH_3 \cdot COO^- + Na^+ + NH_3$$

This reaction is carried out in living organisms by enzymes called proteases in the digestion of proteins (Chapter 5).

7. *Polyfunctional compounds*

Very few compounds of biological importance contain only one functional group. Usually two or three are present in the same molecule to provide the flexibility of behaviour that is needed in the very complex systems of reactions that make up metabolic processes. In general, polyfunctional compounds possess the sum of the properties of the various functional groups that are present in the molecule, though neighbouring functional groups may modify each other's properties in the kinds of way that we have already noticed. Amino acids and hydroxyacids are discussed briefly below. We have selected these two classes because a number of examples of each are of great biological importance. It would be impossible to discuss separately all the varieties of polyfunctional compounds which occur in living systems.

(i) *Amino acids* are compounds containing both an amino group ($-NH_2$) and a carboxyl group ($-COOH$). All the amino acids of biological importance have the $-NH_2$ and $-COOH$ groups attached to the same carbon atom, which also carries a hydrogen atom and some other grouping. Their general formula can therefore be written

$$R \cdot CH(NH_2) \cdot COOH$$

where R represents one of the twenty different groupings that are found in naturally occuring amino acids. The R group may be just hydrogen (in the simplest amino acid, glycine, $NH_2 \cdot CH_2 \cdot COOH$) or a simple hydrocarbon chain, or it may contain other functional groupings such as another carboxyl, another $-NH_2$, a hydroxyl group, etc.

The properties of $-NH_2$ and $-COOH$ groups are not greatly modified by their proximity except in that, since $-NH_2$ is basic and $-COOH$ is acidic, in solutions of biological pH the acids actually exist as salts of themselves

$$^+NH_3 \cdot CHR \cdot COO^-$$

where the carboxyl group has lost a hydrogen ion and the amino group has gained one. Such an ion having opposing charges in different parts of the molecule is called a zwitterion (German *zwitter* = hybrid). In more acid solutions, of course, the carboxyl group will pick up another H^+ and become dissociated while in alkaline solutions the NH_3^+ grouping will lose its H^+

$$^+NH_3 \cdot CHR \cdot COOH \leftrightarrow {}^+NH_3 \cdot CHR \cdot COO \leftrightarrow NH_2 \cdot CHR \cdot COO^-$$
$$\text{low pH} \qquad\qquad \text{pH} \approx 7 \qquad\qquad \text{high pH}$$

(ii) *Hydroxy acids* are compounds containing $-OH$ and $-COOH$ groups. Of particular biological interest is lactic acid ($CH_3 \cdot CHOH \cdot COOH$), the alternative end product to ethanol in anaerobic respiration. Malic acid and citric acid are important intermediates in aerobic respiration

$$\begin{array}{c} COOH \\ | \\ CHOH \\ | \\ CH_2 \\ | \\ COOH \end{array}$$

malic acid

$$\begin{array}{c} COOH \\ | \\ CH_2 \\ | \\ HOC \cdot COOH \\ | \\ CH_2 \\ | \\ COOH \end{array}$$

citric acid

The reactions in which these compounds are involved are those already discussed in connection with the —OH and —COOH functional groups. They are affected only to a slight extent by the presence of the other groups.

8. *Optical isomerism*

Until now, we have not discussed the shapes of molecules. We have

written methane as CH_4 or $H-\underset{\underset{\textstyle H}{|}}{\overset{\overset{\textstyle H}{|}}{C}}-H$ and said that there are four hyd

atoms attached to each carbon atom, but we have not considered how the hydrogen atoms are arranged in space. Are they, as the structural formulae suggest, arranged at the corners of a square, or are they in some three-dimensional configuration? In fact, they lie at the vertices of a *regular tetrahedron* – a figure made up of four equilateral triangles – with the carbon atom at the centre of the tetrahedron (Fig. 4.1).

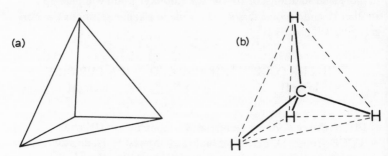

(a)

(b)

Fig. 4.1 (a) Regular tetrahedron.
   (b) Arrangement of H atoms in methane (dotted lines represent the edges of the tetrahedron)

Whenever a carbon atom forms four single bonds, this tetrahedral arrangement is created, though sometimes a little distorted, so that almost all organic compounds have a three-dimensional structure.

One important result of this tetrahedral structure is that a compound in which there are four different groups attached to a single carbon atom can exist in two different forms called, for reasons that will appear later, *optical isomers* or *enantiomorphs*. The carbon atom to which the groups are attached is called an *asymmetric centre*. We can illustrate the way in which this happens in the case of lactic acid. In the lactic acid molecule the four different groups attached to the one carbon atom are CH_3, OH, COOH and H, and the two different ways in which they can be attached are

$$CH_3 \qquad\qquad\qquad CH_3$$
$$\overset{|}{C} \qquad\qquad\qquad \overset{|}{C}$$
$$H^{/}\;\;{}^{\backslash}COOH \qquad\qquad H^{/}\;\;{}^{\backslash}OH$$
$$OH \qquad\qquad\qquad COOH$$

It is not perhaps obvious that these two three-dimensional structures are distinct, or that they are the only two possible ways in which the four groups can be attached. To convince someone of these facts in words is difficult. If you cannot convince yourself of it from the figure, try making models from four matchsticks, stuck into a ball of plasticine to represent the central carbon atom and either painted four different colours or with four differently coloured balls of plasticine stuck on to the ends to represent the attached groups. You should also find that the two forms are related to each other as an object is to its image in a mirror, or as a right-handed screw is to a left-handed one.

The main difference in behaviour between a pair of optical isomers lies in their effect on polarized light. This is a complicated subject, and we will just describe the experimental result. If light is passed through two polaroid filters (the lenses from a pair of sunglasses, for example) the amount of light getting through varies if one of the filters is rotated about an axis along the line joining them (Fig. 4.2). If they are rotated so that no light gets through, and a solution of one of a pair of optical isomers is then placed between the filters, there will be an increase in the amount of light getting through and the second filter will have to be rotated to a new position to cut out all the light. If the experiment

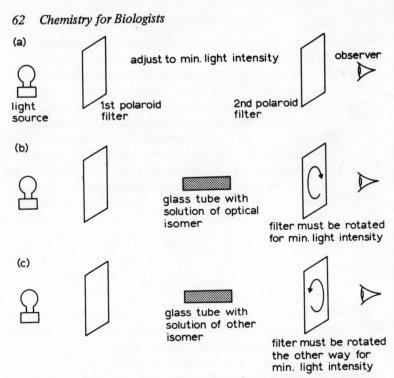

Fig. 4.2 Schematic diagram of apparatus to demonstrate optical activity.

is repeated using a solution of the other optical isomer, the result will be that the second filter has to be rotated to the same extent, but in the opposite direction, to cut out all the light. Solutions of compounds which do not posses an asymmetric centre produce no effect. Compounds which do produce the effect are said to be *optically active* – hence the term optical isomer.

Chemically, a pair of optical isomers are almost indistinguishable. If they are reacted with a compound having no asymmetric centre, they both behave in the same way. If, however, they are reacted with another optically active compound, one enantiomorph will usually react faster than the other, and sometimes one may not react at all.

You may find it helpful in understanding this to use the analogy with right-handed and left-handed screws. Both can pass through a round hole – react with an optically inactive compound – but only a right-handed screw can pass through a right-handed nut.

Most compounds of biological importance are optically active, and it is almost invariably the rule that only one of the enantiomorphs is found in living systems. All the naturally occurring amino acids except glycine, for example, are optically active, and in all cases the four groups H, NH_2, COOH, and R are arranged around the asymmetric centre in the same way.

CHAPTER 5

Compounds of Biological Interest

1. *Carbohydrates – monosaccharides*

Carbohydrates are so called from the fact that they contain hydrogen and oxygen atoms in the proportions of two H to one O, together with carbon atoms, a circumstance which led early workers in the the field to believe that carbohydrates were formed from carbon and water. This view is erroneous, and the H:O ratio is more or less fortuitous.

All carbohydrates consist of chains of carbon atoms (usually six, sometimes five, atoms long) linked into rings and chains by oxygen atoms. In addition, all the carbon atoms carry —OH or —O—→ groups. The simplest carbohydrates contain only one chain of carbon atoms per molecule and are called *monosaccharides*. Glucose, the most familiar of all carbohydrates to the biologist, is a monosaccharide. Its structure is

$$C^6H_2OH$$

$$
\begin{array}{c}
\text{C}^5\text{—O} \\
\text{H} \quad \text{H} \quad \text{H} \\
{}_4\text{C} \quad \text{OH} \quad \text{H} \quad \text{C}_1 \\
\text{HO} \quad \text{C}_3\text{—}\text{C}_2 \quad \text{OH} \\
\text{H} \quad \text{OH}
\end{array}
$$

Notice that this formula is drawn in a kind of diagrammatic perspective, the heavy lines showing the part of the ring which is towards the reader. This is usually done for carbohydrates because of the large number of asymmetric centres (carbon atoms having four different groups attached to them) present in these molecules. The two possible arrangements of groups around each centre can be most easily thought of in this case as two possible choices as to which group goes above and which below the plane of the ring,

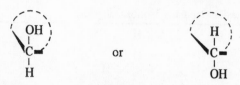

or

The various possible arrangements (there are thirty-two of them altogether) occur in different monosaccharides, some of which occur in nature, while others are only known in the laboratory. A few are listed in Table 5.1.

The carbon atom numbered 1 in the formula for glucose, is singly bonded to two oxygen atoms. It was mentioned in the last chapter that such a situation is often rather unstable; that is the case here. The ring is quite easily broken open between the O and C atoms when glucose is dissolved in acid or alkaline solutions, leading to a carbonyl straight-chain form of the compound which is in fact an aldehyde.

Sugars like glucose, which become aldehydes when the ring is opened, are called *aldoses*.

Since the aldehyde group is strongly reducing, aldoses are reducing agents and give red precipitates on warming with Fehling's solution. They are often referred to as reducing sugars.

When the ring breaks open in this way, carbon atom 1 ceases to be an asymmetric centre, for only three groups are attached to it. If the ring reforms, either of the above-mentioned arrangements can be generated at C_1 – different enzymes select different arrangements – so that the two compounds differing only at this centre are very closely related. Because of this they are both called glucose (α-glucose and β-glucose) and both occur naturally. The form shown on P.64 is α-glucose.

TABLE 5.1
Some Naturally Occuring Monosaccharides

α-glucose	(structure of α-glucose ring)	aldohexose
Galactose	(structure of galactose ring)	aldohexose
Fructose	(structure of fructose ring)	ketohexose
Ribose	(structure of ribose ring)	aldopentose
Ribulose	(structure of ribulose ring)	ketopentose

Problem 5.1.   Draw the structural formula of β-glucose.

In another class of monosaccharides, neither of the end carbon atoms in the chain forms part of the ring, which in this case contains only five members. An example is fructose.

The rings of these compounds are also easily opened, though the results are not aldehydes but ketones.

Such monosaccharides are called *ketoses* and are not reducing sugars. They have no effect on Fehling's solution.

All the monosaccharides that we have discussed so far, have six carbon atoms. They are therefore called *hexoses* (aldohexoses or ketohexoses). Five-carbon monosaccharides (*pentoses*) are also important biologically. Two are included in Table 5.1.

2. *Other carbohydrates*

Carbohydrates are, of course, the main source of chemical energy for living organisms, and it is monosaccharides which provide the raw materials for the complex series of reactions that utilize this energy. For storage purposes insoluble forms of carbohydrate are needed; these are formed by linking together monosaccharide units (or 'residues'). They are linked together by oxygen 'bridges', formed from an ——OH group on each of two monosaccharide molecules by loss of water.

Such a reaction is called a *condensation*. It does not occur directly in biological systems – an intermediate phosphate ester of one of the hydroxyl groups is involved – but the reverse reaction in which an oxygen 'bridge' is broken can be readily carried out by digestive enzymes such as amylase (or, in the laboratory, by boiling with dilute acid).

The products of the linking of monosaccharide units are called *disaccharides* (two monosaccharide units linked), *oligosaccharides* (a few monosaccharide units linked) or *polysaccharides* (many monosaccharide units linked). A wide range of such compounds is possible, depending on the monosaccharide units and the way in which they are attached.

The most familiar of disaccharides is sucrose (ordinary 'sugar') which consists of a molecule of glucose linked to one of fructose by an oxygen bridge between C_1 of α-glucose and C_2 of fructose.

glucose   fructose

Notice that the bridge involves that carbon atom of glucose which would become part of the aldehyde group on ring-opening; sucrose thus has no reducing properties. There is therefore no reaction when sucrose is warmed with Fehling's solution. On prolonged boiling however, the sucrose is broken up into its monosaccharide components and the free glucose formed reduces the Fehling's solution.

TABLE 5.2

Some Complex Carbohydrates

Name	*Type*	*Monosaccharide units (residues)*	*Linking*	*No. of monosaccharide residues*
Sucrose	disaccharide	α-glucose + fructose	glucose C_1 to fructose C_2	2
Maltose	disaccharide	α-glucose + α-glucose	glucose C_1 to glucose C_4	2
Lactose	disaccharide	β-glucose + galactose	galactose C_1 to glucose C_4	2
Starch	polysaccharide	α-glucose + some β-glucose	C_1 to C_4	≈ 500
Cellulose	polysaccharide	β-glucose	C_1 to C_4	≈ 3000
Glycogen	polysaccharide	α-glucose	C_1 to C_4 (and C_1 to C_6)	≈ 1000

Table 5.2 lists a number of complex carbohydrates. Most of them consist of a single long chain of monosaccharides, but the chains in glycogen are branched by occasional glucose residues' having three other residues linked to them at C_1, C_4 and C_6.

Problem 5.2   Which of the disaccharides listed in Table 5.2 will reduce Fehling's solution (a) on warming, (b) on prolonged boiling?

3. *Fats*

Any compound that can be extracted from tissue by a solvent such as ether or benzene is called a *lipid*. These solvents dissolve compounds in which most of the molecule is made up of unsubstituted hydrocarbon chains or rings. Compounds containing many —OH or C $=$ O groups are not usually soluble in ether or benzene. Lipids, then, are compounds which are mostly hydrocarbon; fats are the simplest chemically. A wide range of other lipids occurs in nature, in particular the *steroids* which include a number of vitamins and hormones and the alcohol cholesterol. To discuss them would be beyond the scope of this book however, so we shall restrict ourselves to a brief accound of *fats* and *oils* (fats with a low melting point).

Fats, almost invariably, are esters of glycerol with carboxylic acids called *fatty acids*. A variety of fatty acids is found in fats and oils from various sources, but they all consist of long hydrocarbon chains — either saturated or containing one or two double bonds — with a carboxyl group at the end. In the last chapter we mentioned stearic acid ($(CH_2)_{17}COOH$) which has an eighteen-carbon-atom saturated chain. The ester formed from a molecule of glycerol and three of stearic acid is called tristearin and is the main constituent of mutton fat.

$$
\begin{array}{ll}
CH_2OH & HOOC \cdot CH_2 \cdot CH_2 \cdot CH_2 \cdot CH_2 \cdot CH_2 \cdot CH_2 \ldots \cdot CH_2 \cdot CH_2 \cdot CH_2 \cdot CH_2 \cdot CH_2 \cdot CH_2 \cdot CH_3 \\
CHOH \ \ + & HOOC \cdot CH_2 \cdot CH_2 \cdot CH_2 \cdot CH_2 \cdot CH_2 \cdot CH_2 \ldots \cdot CH_2 \cdot CH_2 \cdot CH_2 \cdot CH_2 \cdot CH_2 \cdot CH_2 \cdot CH_3 \\
CH_2OH & HOOC \cdot CH_2 \cdot CH_2 \cdot CH_2 \cdot CH_2 \cdot CH_2 \cdot CH_2 \ldots \cdot CH_2 \cdot CH_2 \cdot CH_2 \cdot CH_2 \cdot CH_2 \cdot CH_2 \cdot CH_3 \\
\text{glycerol} & \qquad\qquad \text{three molecules of stearic acid}
\end{array}
$$

$$
\begin{array}{l}
\ \ \ CH_2 \cdot OOC \cdot CH_2 \cdot CH_2 \cdot CH_2 \cdot CH_2 \cdot CH_2 \cdot CH_2 \ldots \cdot CH_2 \cdot CH_2 \cdot CH_2 \cdot CH_2 \cdot CH_2 \cdot CH_2 \cdot CH_3 \\
= \ CH \cdot OOC \cdot CH_2 \cdot CH_2 \cdot CH_2 \cdot CH_2 \cdot CH_2 \cdot CH_2 \ldots \cdot CH_2 \cdot CH_2 \cdot CH_2 \cdot CH_2 \cdot CH_2 \cdot CH_2 \cdot CH_3 \\
\ \ \ CH_2 \cdot OOC \cdot CH_2 \cdot CH_2 \cdot CH_2 \cdot CH_2 \cdot CH_2 \cdot CH_2 \ldots \cdot CH_2 \cdot CH_2 \cdot CH_2 \cdot CH_2 \cdot CH_2 \cdot CH_2 \cdot CH_3 \\
\qquad\qquad\qquad\qquad\qquad \text{tristearin}
\end{array}
$$

You can see how close to being a hydrocarbon this fat is.

The fatty acids in vegetable oils are mostly unsaturated ones, such as oleic acid ($CH_3(CH_2)_7CH = CH(CH_2)_7COOH$) and palmitic acid ($CH_3(CH_2)_{14}COOH$). These combine with glycerol in exactly the same way as stearic acid, to form esters, as illustrated above.

Fats are of course energy sources like carboyhdrates. They also are oxidized to carbon dioxide and water, but the reactions appear to take place more slowly. However, more energy is liberated for, if you compare the chemical structures of fat and carbohydrate, you can see that the carbohydrate is already relatively oxidized. Quantitatively, the heat of combustion of tristearin is 40·6 kJ g^{-1} while that of glucose is 15·6 kJ g^{-1}; we quote heats per gramme rather than per mole because the molecular weights of tristearin and glucose are very different.

4. *Proteins*

Proteins are the most versatile of naturally occurring materials. Some are enzymes (indeed all enzymes are proteins), some are hormones (e.g. insulin), some form connective tissue, some are responsible for muscle contraction, some are oxygen carriers, and so on – but all are constructed from amino acids.

The two functional groups that characterize amino acids (the —NH_2 group and the —COOH group) can, as we saw in the last chapter, combine together to form an amide.

$$—NH_2 + HOOC— = —NH·CO —+ H_2O$$

This is the basic way in which proteins are constructed, so, because of its importance, the —NH·CO— link is given a special name, the *peptide bond*.

You will remember that there are twenty naturally occurring amino acids and that all of them can be represented by the general formula

$$H_2N — \overset{\displaystyle H}{\underset{\displaystyle R}{\overset{|}{\underset{|}{C}}}} — COOH$$

In proteins these amino acid units (residues) are linked together into long chains, called *peptide chains*, by amide formation.

$$H_2N \overset{\overset{\displaystyle H}{|}}{\underset{\underset{\displaystyle R_1}{|}}{C}} \overset{\overset{\displaystyle O}{\|}}{C} N \overset{\overset{\displaystyle H}{|}}{\underset{\underset{\displaystyle R_2}{|}}{C}} \overset{\overset{\displaystyle O}{\|}}{C} N \overset{\overset{\displaystyle H}{|}}{\underset{\underset{\displaystyle R_3}{|}}{C}} \cdots \overset{\overset{\displaystyle H}{|}}{\underset{\underset{\displaystyle R_n}{|}}{C}} COOH$$

Here $R_1, R_2, R_3, \ldots R_n$ represent some or all of the twenty possible different side chains that characterize the twenty different amino acids. The almost infinite variety of different proteins found in biological systems results from the very large number of different orders in which amino acids can be arranged along a chain whose length varies from about fifty to some tens of thousands of amino acid residues.

This is not, however, the full story of the structure of proteins, for in the natural state the peptide chain is folded and coiled in a way specific to the particular protein, determined and held in place by various effects. The main one is hydrogen bonding (Chapter 1) between the $>$NH group of one peptide link and the $>$C$=$O group of some other one in another part of the chain. In addition, there are electrostatic forces between the $-$NH$_3^+$ groups present in some side chains and the $-$COO$^-$ groups present in others. One amino acid, cysteine, has an $-$SH group in its side chain. Two cysteine residues in different parts of the chain can link together in a disulphide bridge.

$$H_2N \cdot CH \cdot COOH$$
$$\overset{|}{CH_2}$$
$$\overset{|}{SH}$$
cysteine

$$\ldots\ldots CO \cdot NH \cdot CH \cdot CO \cdot NH \ldots\ldots$$
$$\overset{|}{CH_2}$$
$$\overset{|}{S}$$
$$\overset{|}{S}$$
$$\overset{|}{CH_2}$$
$$\ldots\ldots CO \cdot NH \cdot CH \cdot CO \cdot NH \ldots\ldots$$

Two cysteine residues linking different parts of a peptide chain

Many proteins contain several distinct peptide chains linked in this way. Finally, the actual shapes and sizes of the side groups can influence the ways in which the chains can fold together.

It is a question of current discussion among biochemists whether the detailed shape of protein molecules depends only on these effects and thus on the particular amino acid sequence, or whether the way in which a protein is made in the living organism is also important. At any rate, if the structure is disturbed and broken up the biological properties of a protein are changed irreversibly, so it seems that they must depend almost entirely on the detailed shape of the molecule.

This breaking up of the structure is called *denaturization* and can occur quite easily, since the forces that determine the structure, especially the hydrogen bonds, are rather weak. Boiling a protein solution is sufficient to denaturize it, as in the familiar effect on egg albumin (egg white) of boiling the egg.

To determine the order of the amino acids in the peptide chain of a protein is a very difficult task — it has been carried out completely for only a very few proteins, up till now. Determining the way in which the peptide chains are folded is, if anything, even harder; both these problems are actively occupying many research biochemists at present.

Some proteins contain, beside the peptide chain or chains, a part which is not made up of amino acids. Such a part is called a *prosthetic group* and is often the site of the specific activity of the protein. Haemoglobin, for example, contains a prosthetic group in which there is an iron atom, with which the oxygen carried by haemoglobin is closely associated. Sometimes the prosthetic group can be easily detached from and replaced in the protein; it is not unreasonable to look on some coenzymes as weakly bound prosthetic groups.

Problem 5.3.   Disulphide bridges can be broken by reducing agents, and reformed by oxidizing agents. Most 'home perms' consist of a solution of a reducing agent, and one of an oxidizing agent. The hair is set between applications of the two solutions. Attempt to explain the biochemistry of this process.

5. *Nucleotides*

The biochemistry of most processes carried out by cells involves a

number of molecules of· moderate complexity which serve as
intermediaries of one sort or another. The most familiar example is
probably the ADP–ATP pair; these serve as energy intermediaries,
picking up energy from respiratory reactions and delivering it wherever
it is needed for protein synthesis, muscle contraction, or any other
energy-requiring process. Other intermediaries are concerned in
oxidation and reduction. As we saw in Chapter 3, whenever a
compound is oxidized some other compound must be reduced; the
respiratory oxidation of carbohydrates leads to the reduction of
compounds such as NAD, which are later oxidized (indirectly) by
atmospheric oxygen with the production of energy in a useful form –
usually ATP.

Many of these compounds are *nucleotides* – compounds made up of
three parts: a phosphate group, a pentose (a C_5 carbohydrate), and a
nitrogen-containing base. Of these three parts, phosphate derives from
a typical inorganic oxyacid (Chapter 3); the pentose is either ribose
(section 1 of this chapter) or deoxyribose (formally derived from
ribose by reduction of the hydroxyl group on C_2);

deoxyribose   ribose

while the nitrogen bases are *heterocyclic* compounds, that is,
compounds made up of rings containing two or more different kinds of
atom.* Some of these bases are listed in Table 5.3; the ones containing

---

* Compounds made up of rings containing one kind of atom only are called

homocyclic. Benzene is an example.

TABLE 5.3

Some Heterocyclic Bases

Adenine   purine

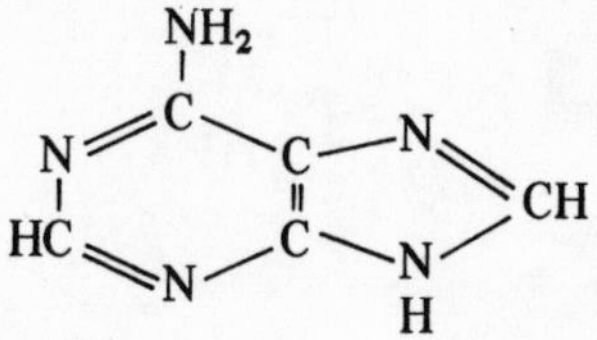

Guanine   purine

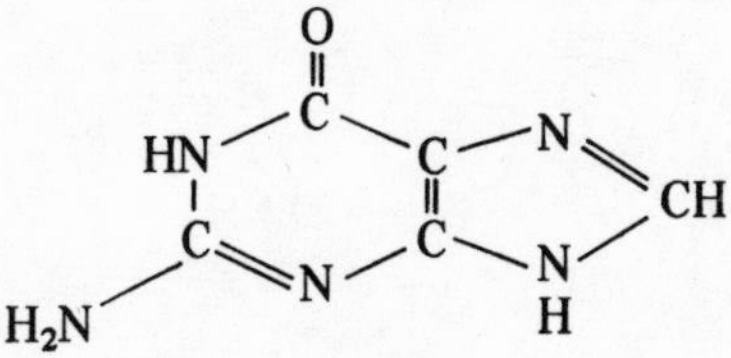

Cytosine   pyrimidine

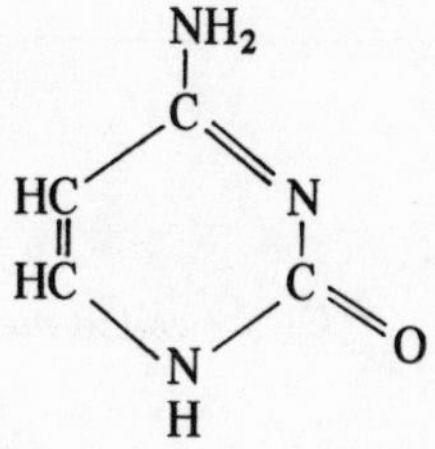

Uracil   pyrimidine

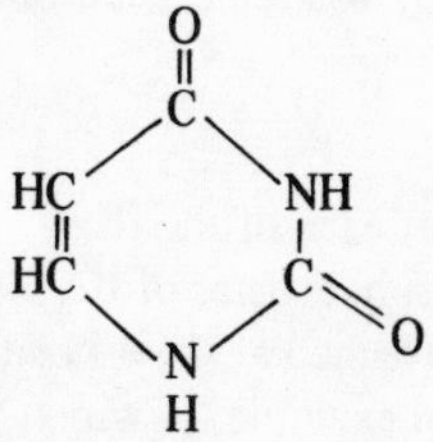

TABLE 5.3 (cont.)

Thymine

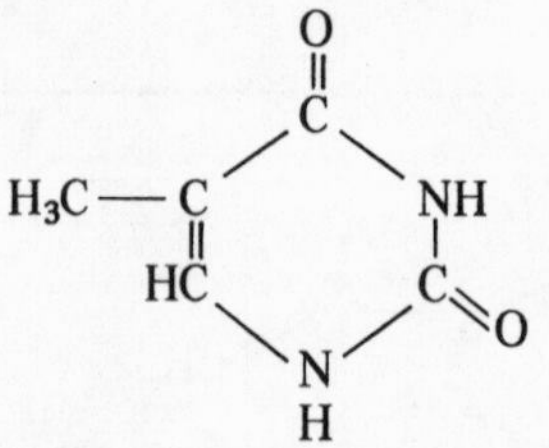

pyridine

Nicotinamide

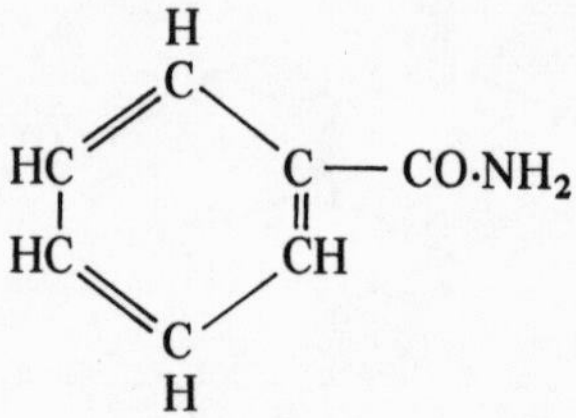

pyridine

the skeleton 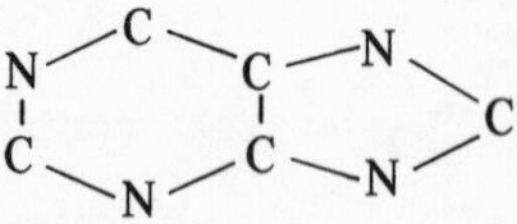 are called *purines*, the ones

based on 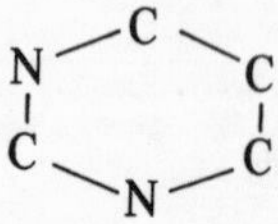 are called *pyrimidines*. Nicotinamide is neither a

purine nor a pyrimidine.

Mononucleotides contain one of each of the three constituents. The phosphate is present as a phosphate ester of the 5-position of the sugar, while the nitrogen base is attached at the 1 position. Adenosine monophosphate (AMP) is a typical example, of which the structure is given on the next page.

phosphate   ribose   adenine

adenosine monophosphate

The familiar energy intermediates ADP (adenosine diphosphate) and ATP (adenosine triphosphate) have the same structure except that the phosphate group is condensed with one (ADP) or two (ATP) more phosphate groups. ATP, for example, is

The oxidation-reduction intermediate NAD is a dinucleotide, that is, it contains two ribose residues and two nitrogen bases. Its full name is nicotinamide adenine dinucleotide and its structure is

Although this structure has a formidable appearance, it is less frightening if you split it up mentally into the two bases, the two ribose residues, and the pyrophosphate link. Its function in oxidation-reduction reactions is carried out in the nicotinamide part of the molecule only, which can be reduced in the following way.

The two hydrogen atoms add on across the heterocyclic ring to form $NADH_2$.

In the nucleotide structural formulae which we have drawn, all the phosphate groups are shown with hydrogen atoms attached to them. This is the form which nucleotides assume in strongly acid solutions. In solutions of biological pH, many of these hydrogen atoms are lost as hydrogen ions, leaving negative charges on the phosphate groups. Various other positive ions, particularly Mg^{2+}, are often attracted to these negatively charged groups in the living cell. These comments also apply to the phosphate groups in nucleic acids, which we shall discuss next.

6. *Nucleic acids*

In NAD, two nucleotide units are held together by a pyrophosphate link. *Nucleic acids* are also made up of nucleotides, but there are very many of them in each nucleic acid molecule, and they are held together by single phosphate groups joined to the ribose residues of two successive nucleotides. The basic structure of a nucleic acid therefore is

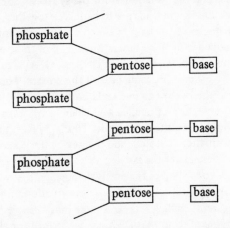

There are two kinds of nucleic acids, called RNA and DNA, which stand for ribonucleic acid and deoxyribonucleic acid respectively. In RNA, the pentose is ribose as in ATP and the phosphate groups are linked to the 5-position on one ribose residue and the 3-position on the

next one. In DNA, ribose is replaced by deoxyribose. DNA is found mainly in cell nuclei, while RNA is found in the cytoplasm. The function of nucleic acids is to store and carry information – in particular the instructions for synthesizing all the various proteins which the organism needs. DNA is the primary source of such information and much, if not all, of the genetic information transmitted from a parent to its offspring is in the form of DNA. One of the functions of RNA appears to be to transport the information contained in the nuclear DNA to the regions in the cytoplasm where protein synthesis actually takes place.

We must now consider how the information is actually carried in the nucleic acid molecule. The answer lies in the nitrogen bases. Although the very long chains of the nucleic acid molecule contain up to 30000 or more nucleotide units, and thus the same number of nitrogen bases, with almost no exceptions only four kinds of base are found in each nucleic acid. DNA contains cytosine (C), guanine (G), thymine (T) and adenine (A); while RNA contains cytosine, guanine, adenine and uracil (U).

The information that is required for the synthesis of a protein is the order in which the amino acids are to be linked together. If we consider a section of a nucleic acid chain made up of three nucleotides, these will carry a sequence of three bases. Since each of these can be one of the four possible bases (C, G, A, T in DNA; C, G, A, U in RNA) there are $4 \times 4 \times 4 = 64$ possible sequences of three bases. This is more than one for each of the twenty amino acids, so that a '*code*' in which a three-nucleotide section of nucleic acid chain (a triplet) represents an amino acid, would be quite practicable. This is, in fact, the way in which the information is stored, and the key to the code has been worked out in detail over the last ten years. The triplet UUU, for example, is the code symbol for phenylalanine.

In order for DNA to transmit genetic information, it must be a very stable molecule (which it is) and there must also be a method for the exact copying of it, so that DNA can be formed for all the many cells produced in succeeding generations from a single parent cell. This method depends on the fact that DNA is not actually found as a single chain of nucleotides such as we have so far described, but consists of two chains coiled around each other in a structure usually called a

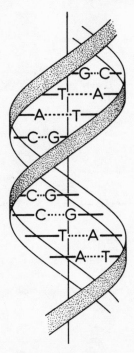

Fig. 5.1 Schematic diagram of helical structure of DNA.

double helix. In this structure the phosphate groups lie outside and the
bases in the centre of the spiral, successive bases from one chain lying
close to successive ones from the other (Fig. 5.1)

It was one of the great breakthroughs of modern biochemistry to
realize that the four bases of DNA can be grouped into complementary
pairs that, when held together by hydrogen bonds, take up the exact
amount of space available inside the double helix. The pairs are cytosine
and guanine and thymine and adenine and the way they pair together is
shown in Fig. 5.2. It is now easy to see that no other pairing would do,
for a pair of pyrimidines would be too small and a pair of purines would
would be too big, while the other possible purine-pyrimidine pairs are
not correctly arranged for hydrogen bonding.

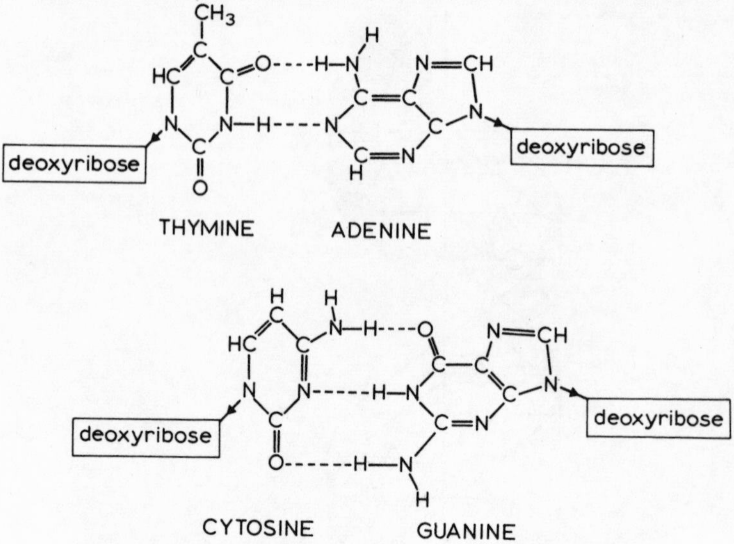

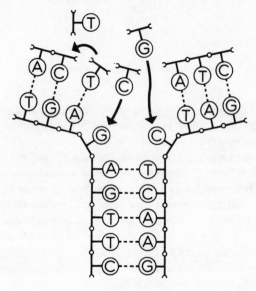

deoxyribose
deoxyribose
THYMINE
ADENINE
deoxyribose
deoxyribose
CYTOSINE
GUANINE

Fig. 5.2 Specific pairing of bases by hydrogen bonding in DNA.

Fig. 5.3 Schematic diagram of helical structure of DNA.

The exact way in which this double strand structure is used to copy DNA is not fully worked out, but it is easy to imagine a process whereby the strands are separated and a new complementary strand is synthesized as a partner for each of the old strands. Fig. 5.3, in which the twisting of the DNA strands has been omitted for clarity, represents this in a schematic way.

CHAPTER 6

Solutions

1. *True solutions and colloids*

Almost all biological processes occur in solution, and the majority of
laboratory chemistry is also carried out in solution. Solutions and their
properties are therefore of considerable interest to the biologist.

All solutions consist of a liquid called the *solvent* in which one or
more other substances, called *solutes*, are dispersed. The amount of
solute that can be dissolved in a given amount of solvent is usually
limited. The largest concentration (p.30) of the solute which can be
dissolved in the solution, is called its *solubility*. If the amount of a
solute in a solution increases (usually because it is being formed by a
chemical reaction which is taking place in the solution) until its
concentration is greater than its solubility, some of the material will
appear as a solid. This phenomenon is called *precipitation*, and the solid
formed is called a *precipitate*. Precipitation can also be caused by
lowering the solubility of a solute by some means. A change in the
temperature or pH of the solution, or the addition of another solvent
are techniques often used in the laboratory to produce this effect.

The solute can be present in solution in a number of different forms,
The simplest solutions, *molecular solutions*, occur when the solute is a
substance having small molecules which, on dissolution, simply separate
and move about independently among the solvent molecules. Solutions
of urea or glucose in water are of this kind, as are most solutions in
organic solvents such as ether or benzene.

We have frequently met with substances which dissociate into ions
in solution. In such *ionic solutions* the various ions move about
independently of one another much as in molecular solutions, but the
electric charges on the particles modify their behaviour in a number of
ways, one of which we shall mention later in this chapter. At the
moment we just notice that an ionic solution must always contain equal

numbers of positive and negative charges to ensure electrical neutrality of the solution as a whole.

The majority of biological solutions are colloidal in nature. There is no very precise definition of a *colloid*, but the term is generally used when one substance is dispersed in another in particles which, though still very small, are significantly larger than the small molecules or ions that are found in true solutions. Roughly, a particle should be thought of as colloidal if its diameter lies between 10Å and 1000Å.* Strictly speaking, if a colloid consists of a solid dispersed in a liquid it should be called a *sol*, and a liquid dispersed in a liquid called an *emulsion*. However, it is common usage to refer to both of these, and sols in particular, as *colloidal solutions*.

Colloidal solutions are of two kinds depending on whether the particles consist of only one single molecule or of a number of smaller molecules. The former case, which is the one usually found biologically, is called a *molecular colloid* while the latter, which is rather unimportant biologically except for the transport of lipids, is called a *micellular colloid*.

The standard chemist's method of separating solids from liquids is *filtration*. The liquid is allowed to soak through a piece of unglazed paper (filter paper) or a disc of sintered glass; this holds back any solid material, while dissolved substances pass through with the liquid. Colloidal particles normally pass through such a filter. In biochemistry filtration is rather rarely used. Instead, when a protein, for example, has been precipitated from solution, it is usually separated from the liquid by *centrifuging*. The mixture of solid and liquid is placed in a tube and rotated very rapidly in a centrifuge. The solid material settles quickly to the bottom of the tube under the action of centrifugal force and the liquid can then be poured off. Colloidal particles are not normally separated out by centrifuging either. However, the ultracentrifuge, which is a centrifuge revolving at an extremely high speed, can separate colloidal particles from the solvent to some extent.

It is possible to find materials which will retain colloidal particles while permitting true solutes to pass through. Cellophane is such a

* $1Å = 10^{-8}$ cm. The distance between two atoms in a molecule is usually of the order of $1-2Å$.

material, and the process of separating a colloid from non-colloid materials by allowing them to diffuse through such a membrane is called *dialysis*. This is the main process which is used in artificial kidney machines; waste products, such as urea, are separated from the blood by allowing them to diffuse through a suitable membrane.

Materials having very large molecules are not usually soluble in anything unless the solvent actually breaks up the molecule. Starch and cellulose are examples of these. Why then are proteins soluble in water? A part of the answer, at least, lies in the fact that many groups in the protein molecule bear an electric charge. As a result of the presence of these groups, the protein molecules as a whole have a net charge, either positive or negative, and the repulsion between these like charges, which causes the molecules to stay apart, is partially responsible for their remaining in solution.

If these charges are reduced in any way the solubility of proteins is diminished. One way in which this can occur is by a change in pH. Since the charged groups in a protein are acidic or basic in nature, a change in pH will alter the extent to which the various groups are ionized and thus the charges which they bear. For any protein there is some pH called the *iso-electric point* at which there is no net change on the protein. At this pH its solubility is at a minimum. The iso-electric point for casein, the protein of cow's milk, for example, is 4·7. As milk becomes sour, lactic acid is liberated and the pH of the solution decreases. As it approaches 4·7 the solubility of the casein becomes smaller than its concentration, and the protein precipitates – this is the familiar curdling of sour milk.

2. *Diffusion and osmosis*

All solutes tend to move from a region of high concentration. If you put a lump of sugar at the bottom of a vessel of water, the sugar will dissolve and initially there will be a high concentration of sugar at the bottom of the vessel and a low concentration at the top. If you leave the solution, sugar molecules will gradually move from the region of high concentration at the bottom to the region of lower concentration further up. If you leave the solution long enough, the concentration will become equal throughout, though the process is slow – this is why

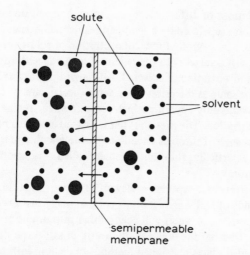

Fig. 6.1 Osmosis − solvent molecules diffuse from region of low
solute concentration to region of higher solute concentration.

we stir our tea!

This phenomenon is called *diffusion* and is a direct consequence of
the Second Law of Thermodynamics (p.27). The initial situation − all
the solute molecules in one region, none in another − is more ordered
than the final situation − some solute molecules in all regions − so that
the change occurs spontaneously, the random motions of the
molecules gradually carrying them into a uniform distribution.
Diffusion will occur equally well if the two regions of differing
concentration are separated by a membrane made of some material
through which the solute can pass, as in the case of dialysis which we
mentioned in the last section.

Diffusion is not confined to solute molecules. Solvent molecules
will also move so as to equalize the concentration in different regions
of a solution. This is difficult to show in a simple experiment such as
the diffusion one we have just described. If, however, a membrane is
used which is permeable to solvent molecules but not solute ones, the
phenomenon is easily demonstrated. Such membranes, called
semi-permeable membranes, are well-known; the skin of a grape is often
used to demonstrate the effect in school laboratories.

If two solutions of different concentration, or a solution and the pure solvent, are separated by a semi-permeable membrane, solvent will move from the region of low concentration of solute (high concentration of a solvent) to the region of high concentration of solute (low concentration of solvent). Although this process is essentially the same as diffusion it is given a special name — *osmosis*. It can be prevented by applying a high pressure to the region of high solute concentration. The pressure that is just sufficient to prevent the movement of solvent through a semi-permeable membrane from pure solvent into a particular solution, is usually called the *osmotic pressure* of that solution.

Osmotic effects are especially relevant to aquatic organisms. Since the body fluids of all living organisms contain many dissolved substances, osmosis of water will occur either into or out of the body, according to whether the organism is a fresh- or salt-water one. All aquatic organisms have developed methods of dealing with the continual water gain or water loss caused by this phenomenon.

Worked Answers to Problems

Problem 1.1

$$C_6H_{12}O_6 = 2C_2H_6O + 2CO_2$$

This is most easily worked out by getting the hydrogen atoms right first and then the carbon atoms. The oxygen atoms can be used as a check.

Problem 1.2

Molecular weights of water and hydrogen are 18 and 2 respectively. The atomic weight of sodium is 23. Therefore 46 g (2 × 23 g) of sodium react with 36 g (2 × 18 g) of water to give 2 g of hydrogen.

Problem 1.3

Calcium has two electrons outside a closed shell, so each calcium atom needs to lose two electrons. Chlorine atoms can accept only one each, so that two chlorine atoms are needed to each calcium and the empirical formula is $CaCl_2$.

Aluminium has three electrons outside a closed shell and so each atom needs to lose three electrons. Each oxygen atom needs two electrons to form a closed shell structure, so that a single aluminium atom cannot provide the right number of electrons for either one or two oxygen atoms. Two aluminium atoms, however, can provide six electrons, enough for three oxygen atoms, leading to the empirical formula Al_2O_3.

Problem 1.4

The sulphate ion has a valency of two and sodium a valency of one, so that two sodium ions combine with each sulphate ion. The formula is therefore Na_2SO_4.

Calcium, Group II, has a valency of two, phosphate a valency of three. We therefore need at least three calcium ions — total valency six — which can be satisfied by two phosphate ions. A bracket round the phosphate symbol is used to show that the whole ion occurs twice — $Ca_3(PO_4)_2$.

Problem 2.1

During Carboniferous times, the energy travelled from the sun to the earth in the form of light which was absorbed by the leaves of plants and converted by photosynthesis into chemical energy, stored in carbohydrates. The energy remained as chemical energy while the plants were gradually changed into oil deposits. When the petrol extracted from the oil was burned in the cylinder of the car, the chemical energy was converted into heat, and some of this heat was converted into kinetic energy by pushing down the piston in the cylinder. The energy was then transmitted from the piston to the wheels of the car, remaining as kinetic energy throughout.

Problem 2.2

The concentration of amylase has been doubled (twice as much amylase in the same total volume of solution) and the concentration of the starch has been tripled. By the equation

$$\text{rate} = k \times [\text{starch}] \times [\text{amylase}]$$

the rate will be six times as great, so that $6 \times 5 = 30$ mg of starch will be hydrolysed in the first minute.

Problem 2.3

$$\text{ethanol} + \text{acetic acid} = \text{ethyl acetate} + \text{water}$$

The water is present in excess, so that the equilibrium constant can be written

$$K = \frac{[\text{ethyl acetate}]}{[\text{ethanol}] \times [\text{acetic acid}]}$$

$$= \frac{0 \cdot 6}{0 \cdot 4 \times 0 \cdot 3} = 5 \cdot 0 \, 1 \, \text{mole}^{-1}$$

Problem 3.1

$$MgO + H_2O = Mg(OH)_2$$

$$SO_3 + H_2O = H_2SO_4$$

(Magnesium oxide is a metal oxide, while sulphur trioxide is a non-metal oxide.)

Problem 3.2

1 1 of 2M HCl contains 2 moles of HCl, so that 0·05 ml contains $2 \times 0 \cdot 00005 = 10^{-4}$ mole. When this is added to 100 ml of water, the concentration will be 10^{-4} mole in 100 ml, or 10^{-3} mole per l. Since HCl is a strong acid, it will be completely dissociated, and so $[H^+]$ will also be 10^{-3} mole per l.

$$pH = - \log_{10}[H^+] = - \log_{10} 10^{-3} = 3$$

The pH of pure water is 7, so that this minute amount of acid has changed the pH by 4 units.

Problem 3.3

Using the equation 3.4,

$$pH = - \log_{10}K + \log_{10}([\text{salt}]/[\text{acid}])$$

Since the acetic acid and sodium acetate concentrations are the same, $[\text{salt}]/[\text{acid}] = 1$, and

$$pH = - \log_{10}K + \log_{10}1$$
$$= - \log_{10}(1 \cdot 9 \times 10^{-5}) + 0$$
$$= 4 \cdot 72$$

Problem 3.4

(a), (b) and (d)

(a) Mg is oxidized to Mg^{2+}, H^+ (from HCl) is reduced to H_2.

(b) Ca is oxidized to Ca^{2+}, H_2 is reduced to H^-.

(c) Not an oxidation-reduction reaction. Ca^{2+} and Cl^- are unchanged, while H and O remain (formally) H^+ and O^{2-} in H_2O.

(d) H^- from CaH_2 is oxidized to H_2, H^+ from water is reduced to H_2.

Problem 5.1

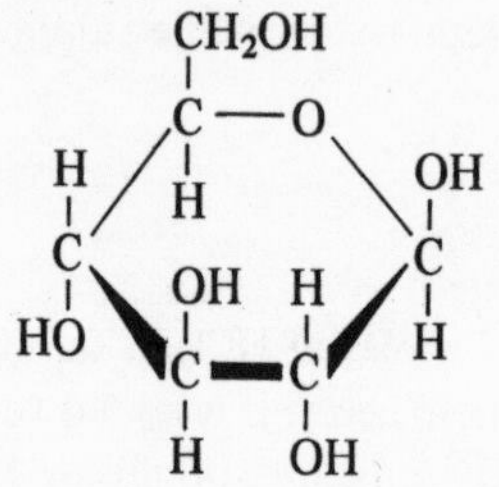

$$CH_2OH$$

$$C - O$$

H — C — H ... OH

HO — C ... OH — H — C — H

C — C

H   OH

Problem 5.2

(a) Maltose and lactose — both contain at least one glucose residue with C_1 free.

(b) Sucrose — the reducing sugar component (glucose) is linked to fructose at C_1. This link is broken on boiling, freeing the reducing part of the molecule.

Problem 5.3

Application of the reducing solution breaks many of the disulphide bridges which play a part in determining the structure of keratin, the protein of hair. The hair is then set, and application of an oxidizing solution causes new disulphide bridges to form, stabilizing the new arrangement of the peptide chains, and fixing the hair in the way in which it has been set.

Index

References to tables are given in italics. Where there are several references to a particular subject, the most important one, or the one which defines a particular term, is given in bold type.

lipids 70, 85
long periods 12

magnesium *5, 10*, 36, 79
magnesium hydroxide *37*
magnesium oxide *37*
malic acid 59
maltose *69*
mass action, law of 30
membrane, semi-permeable 87
metals 2, 4, **36**
methane 49, *50*, 51
   bonding in 15
   shape of 60
methanol *52*
methyl acetamide 58
methyl group 51
methylamine 56
micellular colloid 85
milk, curdling of 86
mixture 2, 4
molar 30
mole 8, 30
molecule 2
molecular colloid 85
molecular solution 84
molecular weight 7
mononucleotides 76
monosaccharides 64
multiple bond 51
mutton fat 70

NAD 74, 77
NADH$_2$ 79
negative ion 13
newton 25
nicotinamide *76*, 76
nicotinamide adenine dinucleotide 77
nitrate *39*
nitric acid *39*, 40
nitrogen *5, 10*, **35**
   bases containing 74, 77, 80
   covalent bonding in 18
non-metal 36
nucleic acids 79ff.
nucleotide 53, 73ff., 79
nucleus, atomic 8
nucleus, cell 80

OH group **52**, 56, 64
oils 70
olefins 51, 53
oleic acid 71
oligosaccharides 68
optical isomerism 60
optically active 62
osmosis 88
osmotic pressure 88
oxalic acid *57*
oxidation **45**ff., 74, 78
   of alcohols 53
oxide ion 15n., **36**, 40
oxides 36ff.
oxidizing agent 45, 73
oxyacids 39, 74
oxygen 2, *5*, 6, *10*, **35**, 45, 46, *47*, 74
   bridge 67

pairing of bases in RNA and DNA 81
palmitic acid 71
pentose 67, 74
peptide bond 71
peptide chain 71, 72
periodic table 9ff., 36
pH **43**, 56, 79, 86
phenylalanine 80
phosphate esters 53, 68
phosphate group 74, 79
phosphate ion 19, *39*, 39
phosphoric acid *37*, 38, *39*, 39, 45
phosphorus *5, 10*, 36
phosphorus pentoxide *37*
polarized light 61
polyanions 40
polybasic acids 45
polyfunctional compounds 58ff.
polyphosphates 39
polysaccharides 68
positive ions 13
potassium *5, 10*, 11
potassium dichromate *47*
potassium hydroxide *37*, 38
potassium oxide *37*
potassium permanganate *47*, 53
potential energy **22**, 26
precipitate 84
propane *50*
prosthetic group 73